THEY NEVER TOLD ME THAT AT VET SCHOOL

*Life as seen by Vets
and what they don't tell you
happens in the real world*

G. Inskip

ISBN-13: 9798636020257

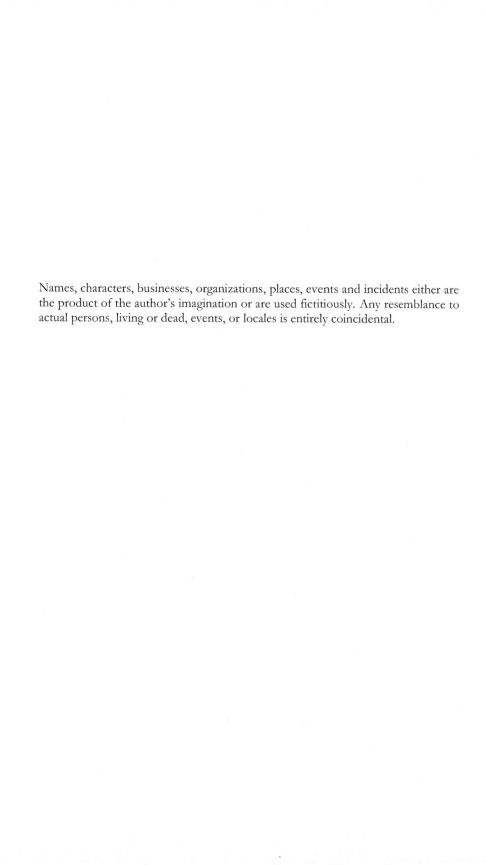

DEDICATION

*To my family; who always taught me to follow my dreams,
no matter how ridiculous they seemed.*

CONTENTS

ACKNOWLEDGMENTS

To Alasdair, Chris, Jayne, Steph, Lynn and Claire –
you taught me everything I needed to know
and much more besides.

PROLOGUE

To work... or not to work?

My name is Gwen Inskip and I graduated from Liverpool University in the summer of 2011 after five exhilarating, terrifying, ultimately enjoyable years at vet school. At that point my brain promptly decided it'd had enough seriousness for a year or five and went on strike for a couple of months. It desperately needed to recover from the arduous rigors of revision, finals and the subsequent alcohol poisoning which occurred on the traditional Grad Holiday to one of the Greek islands. So, while a good proportion of my friends found jobs and became responsible, tax-paying members of the working population, or went gallivanting off on adventures in exotic locales, I cluttered up my mother's spare bedroom, lived out of her fridge, and became the resident dog-walker extraordinaire. Oh, and slept. A lot.

Until one day I happened to take a look at my bank balance and realised it appeared decidedly unhealthy. Five years of living off student loans, and whatever cash could be earned in my admittedly limited summer holidays which were not taken up by compulsory work experience, did not a happy bank manager make. This, along with a staggering degree of boredom – I wasn't the sort of person who could tolerate extended periods of mental or physical inactivity – prompted me to embark upon my search for employment; a task more fraught with difficulties than I had initially realised.

A quick consultation of the British Veterinary Association's flagship journal, The Vet Record, jobs section yielded a goodly number of likely looking possibilities, many of whom were happy to take on the added responsibility of a new, wet-behind-the-ears graduate, with remarkably little effort on my part. However, careful scrutiny of said positions revealed the first of many hurdles I would have to overcome before I would eventually find success.

I feel as though, at this point, I should probably take a moment to educate my readers on the sheer magnitude of Three Letter Acronyms – TLAs – that are apparently crucially important to anyone entering any form of medical profession. And also to make any apologies beforehand should they thoroughly confuse, discombobulate or generally disorientate anyone. I shouldn't worry; most Vet Students or new graduates find themselves in the same boat much of the time. It's either sink or swim, and you get the hang of it eventually.

At the time, being young, idealistic and, most importantly, incredibly naïve, I was determined to find a mixed practice position, thus enabling me to work with large and small animals, preferably in the North West of England, from whence I hailed. Although I didn't know it at the time, this desire was destined to prolong my quest for several months, even after many of my friends had given up their dreams and sacrificed their souls on the altar of one hundred percent small animal practice. I have since reached the conclusion that obstinacy is the true flaw in my character, as I considered giving up rainy days outside among the stock for a nice, dry consulting room, and Mrs Harrington-Smythe's dearest, darling Pekinese a sacrifice.

One of the many problems with my search for gainful employment that would satisfy my bewildering love – obsession – of cattle was truly mixed practices seemed to be a dying breed. Between the financial pressures on agriculture as a whole, the milk price in particular, and the development of large, corporate practices able to offer clients state-of-the-art products and services, smaller, independent mixed practitioners are rapidly finding themselves forced out of the market. As a commentary on the veterinary profession, and the veterinary industry, I will admit to finding this occurrence somewhat distressing. Having experienced a number of practices of all kinds during both University and since graduating, I'll be sad to see the eventual demise of the small, independent veterinary surgery. As a profession we ought to be encouraging diversity and independent thinking, rather than commercial conformity, and as an industry I suspect we'll lose much of our good humour and spirit when the last one closes.

However, as a new grad, I knew very little of this sea-change in the profession I had embarked upon, and my answer to this particular problem was to merely expand my search criteria. Instead of confining myself to the North West, I decided I would be willing to take a job anywhere someone would consider employing me. This opened up a whole world of new adventures and possibilities, once a steady stream of interviews began to arrive in my inbox.

Over the next few months my poor, little, hard-done-by VW Polo traversed the length and breadth of the country. My search for employment took me west to Carmarthen, east to Whitby, south to Dis in Lincolnshire and as far north as Huntley in Aberdeenshire. The people I met on my travels ranged from the unexpected, to the sublime, and every possible combination in between, simply proving the old adage that it takes all sorts

A fairly adept description of the veterinary industry, all things considered.

The vast majority of my interviews occurred over an eight-week period during the winter of 2011/12; possibly one of the worst winters Britain had experienced in the last few decades, which certainly tested the Polo's all-weather, all-terrain capacity to the limit.

CHAPTER ONE

Whitby

My jaunt across country to Whitby didn't have a particularly auspicious start... and rapidly went downhill from there.

It had snowed heavily the night before, and the fluffy white stuff was still falling at half past six in the morning as I set off for my 11 o'clock interview. Usually I dislike having to follow lorries on the road, but that day I had never been so grateful for them to blaze the trail for me. I quite happily set my wheels in their tracks and grimly tried to see where I was going through the closest thing to a blizzard Lancashire had seen in decades.

The drive over the notoriously treacherous A66, and the North York Moors, had me gripping my steering wheel in a white-knuckled grasp, and I was genuinely astonished my poor little car actually managed to make it over some of those hills.

At the end of my journey, the practice I was looking for was down a side-street, behind another house, along a very narrow drive. Understandably, I ended up getting lost. A quick phone call later, unfortunately revealing I'm a little iffy on the difference between my left and right, I was in possession of the correct directions and finally arrived at my destination. Only a quarter of an hour late.

The surgery itself was a moderate-sized mixed practice that had been on the premises for at least a couple of decades, and had a steady stream of clients, both of the large and small variety. I managed a quick nose at the reception and a couple of darkened internal rooms before I was whisked passed the desk into the hallowed ground of the vets' office to meet my prospective employer.

The surgery itself seemed well laid out, with two reasonably sized consulting rooms leading onto a corridor at the back where the dispensary was kept.

"I come out here to think without the client watching me," the practice owner, a tall, greying, middle-aged man called Joseph Dale, who was currently giving me the grand tour, confided. "Or to stare at the drugs and wonder what on earth I can give it. Sometimes I just come out to escape from the client if they're really annoying."

I smiled and said nothing. The escape corridor was a little cramped and crammed with shelves containing all manner of pills and potion, which I had to admit I found a little intimidating. I only recognised a handful of the medications they kept in stock, and the rest of them I couldn't even begin to guess their use. But what was even more horrifying was his response to my enquiry about the computer system the practice used. I had experience with a few of the different veterinary systems, having done work experience in a number of practices, and I thought it would be a good example of my knowledge and usefulness as a new grad, baby vet.

"We don't use one," he scoffed, pointing to a filing cabinet overflowing with A5 index cards. "We've never had a problem with our hand-written system so far. So, I don't see the point of wasting money forking out for an expensive computer system that's probably only going to crash anyway."

At this point, I must admit I experienced the first of many strobing warning lights; *danger, danger, Will Robinson!*

I have seen what the majority of vet's handwriting is like, and I didn't envy the person who was tasked with deciphering it. The long-suffering grimace on a passing veterinary nurse's face seemed to only corroborate my thoughts. Swallowing down my unease, I smiled and followed my guide deeper into the guts of the building. It felt dim, dark and a bit dank.

My prospective employer waved a hand toward the room where the smell of damp seemed to emanate from, calling it; "farm washing."

Amongst the expected forest of olive-green waterproof leggings and parlour tops, I recognised several plastic, disposable calving gowns also hanging up to dry. I liked those gowns, although I always looked like a child playing dress-up, as they were made with the stereotypical male farm vet in mind, and I'm five feet two. However, I have never managed to get one off at the end of a caesarean without tearing it apart.

"They get washed and re-sterilised," my guide said when I commented on how much I liked the way the gowns managed the almost impossible task of keeping my clothing somewhat clean. "Saves money, and the planet."

I fought a losing battle with my eyebrows as they steadily rose up my forehead but managed a suitably polite reply. I was slightly dubious as to how many washes a gown could take, as they were made of a similar material to the average household bin liner. Most likely he spent more in time, electricity and water recycling used gowns than he would if he used a new one each time. Unfortunately, concerning this practice, a hole was being formed, and rapidly becoming filled with pigeon.

Our next step was to go upstairs to the flat, which was the accommodation boasted of in the advert, and a must have for someone like me who was planning on moving all the way across the country for the job. The flat was spacious enough, with stained pine-panelled walls and Paisley carpet seemingly regurgitated directly from the 1970s. Unfortunately, the damp odour did not remain downstairs with the farm washing. Instead it chased us into both the bedroom and bathroom, before we finally managed to lose it in the kitchen.

"The appliances aren't staying," Joseph stated bluntly, referring to the washer, microwave, kettle and fridge-freezer that populated the space. "Vicky is taking them with her. The mattress too, but the bedframe is staying."

Be still my beating heart. I could hardly contain my excitement.

"The bedframe is broken," the departing Vicky later confided in a moment when her boss left us alone. "My boyfriend jumped on it a month ago and broke a few of the slats. You need to be careful not to fall through it."

Lunchtime rolled around and I was pleasantly surprised to find a rep was coming to take us all to the pub. So far it was the best part of the day.

Since we were in Whitby, I opted for the scampi and chips. Unfortunately, because that was how my day, month, year was going, it wasn't particularly good scampi. However, I might be spoilt. My boyfriend came from a fishing community and the fish I had been eating for the past five years had to first stand up to his intense scrutiny. But I kept my mouth shut, ate my free dinner and listened to the rep try her hardest the sell the practice, something they likely didn't want and wouldn't use. Joseph didn't strike me as the sort of man/boss who liked new products when the old worked just as well. I wondered how long they were planning to keep me, and whether I would be able to make it home.

After lunch, Joseph had been booked on a farm call, and decided I should come along to get an idea of what the clients were like. I had already made my mind up about the practice, and despite how desperate my finances looked, I didn't think it and I would suit. Regardless, I put my boots and waterproofs in the back of his car and off we went up onto a remote moor.

The farm itself was on a particularly windswept piece of moorland; a grey, ramshackle building that looked like the only reason it was still standing was the climbing ivy covering three of its four walls. A crooked, corroding gate stood guard over an overgrown, weed-strewn garden, looking as though it hadn't seen any form of care in the last ten years. The wall supposedly holding the garden in was collapsed in several places and broken by roots in others.

It didn't look promising.

I opened the car door and almost had it ripped from my fingers by the prevailing winds. Ice bit at my face and hands as I struggled to shiver my way into my hat, polar buff and waterproofs. Trudging through the ankle-deep muck that covered the yard, corroding gates hanging half off their hinges, I narrowly avoided falling into a slurry-disguised hole due to the last-minute warning from my prospective employer.

The farmer, a bent, wizened man with a florid wind-burnt face and stooped back, led us into a dark shed that looked as though it would fall on top of us at the next stiff gust. Thirty cattle of indeterminate breeding were chained by the neck in a byer, the muck and straw so deep I wondered whether I was going to lose my boots if I stepped into it. The cow we'd come to see was lying down in the furthest section of the byer and by the time we reached her I noticed Joseph had pulled a high-powered torch out of his pocket. The bright light helped a little, but the other cows were still merely darkish blobs at the edges of the beam.

Our patient gave a mournful moo and gazed at Joseph with large, dark, sorrowful eyes. He bustled about, asking a series of rapid questions while performing a speedy, but thorough, clinical examination, as I held the torch and tried not to sink into the muck.

"She's got milk fever," the farmer grumbled in a Yorkshire accent so thick it was like tar. I could barely decipher the individual words, but thankfully Joseph didn't seem to have the same problem. "Calved yesterday. Girt big bull-calf. Been down since."

From the noises Joseph was making he seemed to agree with the farmer's diagnosis. The cow was suffering from a lack of calcium in the blood, which meant, due to the sudden demand on her body for calcium to produce milk for her calf, she had an insufficient dietary supply, and couldn't mobilise enough from her own bones to meet the demand. The classical presenting signs are a freshly calved cow, generally older, lying down with her head tucked into her flank. Cattle suffering from this condition will mostly appear dull, have cold extremities and lower than normal body temperatures. If left untreated paralysis of the gut muscles can lead to bloating, rapid heart rate, unconsciousness and eventually death.

It is a very common diagnosis, especially among dairy cattle or old beef cows. Fortunately, it is also relatively easily treated. A bottle of calcium solution plus some phosphorous into the vein, another bottle under the skin, and some cows will walk straight off the needle.

This particular cow didn't. But she did look much happier by the time we squelched our way out of the byer.

The farmer invited us into the house for a cuppa and, considering the freezing temperature, it was accepted with alacrity. As we reached the back door, I began to take off my boots, as they were covered in muck and we were about to enter a house. My mother would have a fit if I traipsed even a quarter of the amount of mud on my soles onto her carpets, and I generally assumed most people were of the same opinion. The farmer trudged directly inside without bothering, and Joseph discretely shook his head before following. Eyebrows sliding upward I intrepidly entered the house.

Inside it was as dark and dim as the byer had been. The only light source came from a weak overhead bulb and the struggling fire. It might have been the low light, or the obvious trail of farm-yard muck, but it was nigh on impossible to see the colour of the carpet beneath the squares of filthy cardboard obviously laid to help contain the mess.

I struggled to repress the desire to wrinkle my nose, or, failing that, breathe through my sleeve to negate the overpowering smell of old cooking fat, damp house and neglect. There was stuff piled high on every surface, some of it teetering dangerously, the whole place seemingly defying every possibly physical law. When I was handed a cracked mug of weak tea that didn't look as though it had seen soap and water in my lifetime, and instructed to "sit myself down" my first thought was *where?* My second was I was glad I still had my waterproofs on.

I perched gingerly on the edge of a chair, trying not to upset the delicate equilibrium of the stack that was my nearest neighbour. Wrapping my frozen hands around the mug I was grateful for its warmth as I pretended to drink and tried to decipher the conversation going on around me.

I have generally always been able to understand accents, even the apparently impenetrable West Cork dialect of the pig farmer I had spent two weeks with in the summer of first year. However, that evening, as far as I could make out, he was speaking another language.

Eventually, Joseph seemed to realise it was getting dark, and I still had a three-hour journey to make in the snow before I could get back home. We returned to the practice and I collected my car, wolfed down half a packet of chocolate digestives to fortify myself for the marathon drive ahead of me, and set off.

It was still snowing.

Once again, I have never been so thankful for lorries in my life. The return journey was a nightmare. Snowdrifts at least six feet tall lined either side of the A66, as snow clogged up my windscreen in a manner no amount of wiper action or screen wash could clear. I could barely see more than a handful of feet in front of my bonnet. I attached myself to the back of a lorry the whole way, fervently praying my poor little engine could make it up the steep hills. I don't think my speedometer went much above forty miles an hour the entire way back to my mother's house.

I arrived home at nearly ten o'clock, and as I fell cold and exhausted into bed, I vowed *never again*.

CHAPTER TWO

Dis

At the end of January, I had an interview down in Lincolnshire, at a seven-vet mixed practice with a small animal bias. After a long, lonely journey down the M6 the night before to make use of my Aunt's spare room in Shipston, I set off early on that wintery morning for my one o'clock interview a couple of hundred miles away. The drive was boring, but far less harrowing than my previous eastbound cross-country trek, and I arrived in good time after shoe-horning my car into the closest parking space to the practice I could find.

The surgery was clean and well laid out, a large reception-come-waiting room led off onto three sizable, light and airy consult rooms that were easy to manoeuvre around and packed with all the gadgets a girl could dream of. The staff seemed very friendly, the nursing team happy to stop while having a cup of tea and chat to the nervous-looking interviewees taking up space in their breakroom.

"We've got a really good team here at the moment," the head nurse said, passing around a biscuit tin as I perched on the edge of a truly ancient leather sofa that would have swallowed me whole had I allowed it. "Everyone gets on really well, and we're all just the right amount of crazy to cope with anything thrown at us."

I had since learned 'just the right amount of crazy' was a good thing to have in any practice environment, but then I was unaware of that fact. So, I simply smiled and nodded and sipped my tea.

"What is the practice like on a day to day basis?" I asked, curious to get an employee view of the place now the partners had given me their facts and figures. Our tutors had always advised us to question the staff and the outgoing vet about any potential employer, as this tended to illuminate any issues ongoing with the practice.

It seemed like a decent job; one night in six on call, a four-and-a-half-day week split between the main practice in Dis and the smaller branch practice about a fifteen minute drive away. The wage package wasn't anything to be sniffed at either; twenty-five thousand a year plus a practice-owned house to live in for as long as necessary, and a surgery equipped with all the toys a baby vet could wish for. They had purchased a digital x-ray machine, eighteen months previously, owned a mid-range ultrasound scanner, several lab machines for in-house blood workups and a couple of different sized endoscopes for diagnostic evaluation of the intestinal tract and respiratory tree. On paper it appeared to possess everything that could make my little heart beat faster. It wasn't a big farm practice, but it still had enough large animal work to keep me happy and my hand in. The only downside seemed to be the practice's location in a town approximately several hundred miles from the nearest civilisation.

"Busy enough," a vet who was a couple of years my senior cheerfully answered my question as he somewhat viciously bit into a truly epic sandwich. "Not so busy you don't have time to think, but enough work to keep us out of mischief. It gets a bit manic around lambing and calving season, but I don't think you'll find a mixed practice in the country that doesn't."

"What's the support like for new grads?" I continued. He had been with the practice since graduation, so was a good source of information about how I might be treated should I get the position.

"It's good. There's always someone around to ask for help, and you don't get left alone with surgery or out of hours until you're comfortable, and more importantly, competent enough to cope by yourself," he returned without flinching, obviously happy with his lot in life. "It's much better than some places my friends started at, just getting thrown in at the deep end and left to sink or swim."

That was a relief. I had heard horror stories from some of my newly employed friends that were enough to make me shudder. I was confident in my abilities and knowledge, but I was also clever enough to realise being left to my own devices at this crucial stage of my career could be severely detrimental to my growth as a clinician. How was I supposed to improve, to grow as a professional, if there was no one around to correct my mistakes?

"It's a lot flatter than I'm used to," I said a little while later as I was following one of the partners around the practice, reviewing the rooms, equipment and commensuration package they were offering.

I come from Lancashire, not too many miles removed from the Cumbrian border and the Lake District: a county of hills and valleys. Being able to see the horizon without even a hillock to disturb the evenness of the terrain was somewhat disconcerting for me. Lincolnshire was a county that I could get used to cycling in.

A farmer leaning through the hatch overheard my comment and cackled somewhat gleefully.

"It's the sorta place where you could watch a dog run for four days," he announced with a distinct sense of pride.

I wasn't certain I would ever get used to it. But the practice was a good opportunity and I hoped when my interview ended, I would soon be in with a fighting chance of gaining employment. They still had a couple of candidates left to speak to, but they would let me know at the beginning of the following week whether I was successful.

Fingers crossed.

The journey back to my aunt's house wasn't so uneventful.

All seemed to be going just swimmingly, until I reached the point where the A14 merged with the M6, and then utter chaos ensued. Traffic ground to a complete standstill. Flashing blue lights and sirens screaming up the hard shoulder were never a good omen for anyone involved, and usually meant a very long wait for those queuing behind them. It turned out there had been a three-car pile-up on the roundabout itself, requiring the intervention of all three of our emergency services. Several ambulances whizzed people away to hospital, although I learned on the news later on there were thankfully no fatalities. It took well over an hour to get the whole mess straightened out and the grid-locked traffic sluggishly moving once again.

By that point I had listened to an entire *My Chemical Romance* album, likely managing to disturb the drivers of the cars on either side of me. Well, what else was a girl supposed to do in stationary traffic, listening to loud music aside from sing, head bang and air-drum on the steering wheel?

It was once again another late-night drive. I was beginning to think my trips east were somehow cursed.

I didn't get the job.

What I didn't realise was the veterinary industry was changing right before my eyes. With the addition of a seventh veterinary school producing newly graduated vets, the market was being flooded, and finding work was more difficult than ever. By Christmas time, in years gone by, roughly around ninety-five percent of the graduated cohort had found positions, whereas in my year-group that figure had dropped to seventy-five percent, and it didn't look as though it was going to get any easier.

Thankfully, for my dwindling bank balance, I managed to pick up a few weeks of locum work at the small animal branch surgery near home where I had been doing voluntary shifts since the beginning of January. One of the vets had hurt her back and was signed off sick for at least a month until she was capable of the amount of standing and movement a day working in a vets requires. Not only was this work great for my CV, and kept me in the black, I enjoyed working with a great team of vets, nurses and ancillary staff. This time enabled me to learn some of my very first real-life lessons about how to interact with the public professionally, how to function in a practice environment, and exactly how important a cup of tea was in the grand scheme of things.

In some cases, perhaps the most important thing in the world!

CHAPTER THREE

Co. Durham

The final week of February had me once again behind the wheel of my overworked little car, heading back over the A66 into County Durham. I had applied for a job in a small, three-vet mixed practice located in the murky hinterland between Durham, Newcastle and Gateshead, roughly a two-hour journey from my home. Thankfully the snow had finally stopped besieging the country, making my eastward-bound expedition far more pleasant than the last time I had ventured forth on this particular road.

I was instructed to arrive at "Twelve-ish" and given in-depth directions including simple instructions that happily spoke quite comfortably to my own manner of navigation; "Turn right at the Brown Horse pub," and "when you see the King's Head go right at the junction."

This prospective employer, I thought, obviously understands the inner workings of the average vet's mind very well.

It was a relatively easy drive, through nicely rolling countryside, once I had finally left the dull, grey tarmac of the main roads behind. The ups and downs, hills and valleys suited me just fine, as I tended to feel a little uncomfortable surrounded by too much flat land, and were redolent of my native Lancashire. At one point I found myself stopping for a quick loo break in a quaint village, containing a pub for every five houses, and proudly boasting of being the birthplace of

Jeremiah Dixon, one of the founders of the iconic trans American train line; The Mason-Dixon line. Of course that meant I spent the remainder of my journey humming *Dire Straits 'Sailing to Philadelphia'*. It could have been worse.

My travels ended at a village cut in half by the busy A691. The main part of the village consisted of a single high street lined by bakeries, restaurants, hairdressers, a Spar and a garage. A pub and a church stood opposite one another at the far end of the street, and the vet practice was conveniently located equidistant between the two. I parked on a side street and meandered my way into the small courtyard serving as a staff carpark for the surgery and took a moment to study the building.

It was a couple of car-lengths long and reasonably narrow, with period stone facing, masonry crumbling in a few places, and a bewildering number of entrance doors. I took a chance and cracked open the middle of the three, poking my head around to reveal, to my relief, a small waiting room with a bench on two walls, a hatch with frosted glass windows and two doors I presumed led onto consulting rooms. A black board with white detachable letters listed a number of offered procedures and their prices. Evidently, I was in the right place.

The whole room couldn't have fitted more than four people in it at once, and that was without adding their pets into the equation. It was a lot more... compact... than I was expecting.

I chewed my lip and approached the hatch, not exactly certain what I should expect. A woman in her mid-forties was seated at a computer in an office reflecting similar proportions to the waiting room, papers arranged with a sense of organised chaos on every available surface around her. It looked a little like my own desk whenever I had to write a dissertation or essay for university. I didn't doubt that what looked like disorder to me made perfect sense to someone else.

After a moment of my hovering she noticed my presence and her expression transformed from the mildly unnerving, intimidating lines of concentration, to a pleasant, welcoming smile.

"Can I help you?" she enquired, her voice a milder, warmer version of the somewhat harsh Newcastle accent I had been expecting.

"I'm here for an interview at twelve," I returned, feeling more tentative than was my usual habit.

"You must be Gwen," she said, briefly glancing at an open ring-binder with a lined page titled with the day's date, my name in capitals beside it in full view. "I'm Leah; nurse/receptionist, jack of all trades. Andrew is on his way back from a farm call, he shouldn't be long now. In the meantime, why don't I show you around the practice?"

Around the practice inferred far more square footage to the place than actually existed. To the far side of the reception-come-office, two consulting rooms sat catty-corner to one another with the dispensary wedged between them, which became distinctly claustrophobic with both of us in it. Several shelves lined the walls, cluttered with a dazzling array of medications and a small sink unit jammed tightly into the corner. The front consulting room was a decent size with a sash window to the outside world, and, I saw with a sigh of relief, a laptop computer running veterinary software quietly humming to itself on a stainless-steel table. The second consulting room was an internal space and more cramped than the first, but it too boasted its own computer, albeit one squeezed onto the end of a shelf in the dispensary.

We reversed our steps back through the office to a reasonably sized kennel room with a stepped concrete floor that had several drainage channels cut into the lower half, leading to a small hole in the outside wall. Each of the kennels had occupants, most of whom looked mournful or sedated. I was surprised how busy they seemed for such a tiny practice.

"Sometimes we do sheep caesars in here during lambing season,"

Leah informed me, obviously noting my perusal of the flooring with a slight degree of alarm. "We're chocka at the moment with lambings and calvings, but it should quiet down in another couple of months. It's mostly sheep and beef around here now since Foot and Mouth, so the farm work tends to be seasonal."

From the kennel room we moved into a short corridor, a door to the outside on my left, a sink with a mixer tap and surgical scrub directly in front and a glass sliding door opening onto the operating theatre to my right. Currently there was a dog on the table, covered in green surgical drapes and a tall male vet in his forties engaged in the removal of its ovaries and uterus seated beside it. A younger blond woman with a stethoscope in her ears monitored the dog's heart and respiratory rate beside the anaesthetic machine.

As with the rest of the practice I had seen thus far, the theatre was of diminutive proportions, and would struggle to admit more than two persons comfortably. Yet it contained everything required for surgery; table, anaesthetic machine, pulse oximeter and surgical consumables. As I had often observed in my own situation; size wasn't everything.

"This is Carl, our other partner, and Jess, another nurse," Leah introduced us as her colleagues responded with cheerful, welcoming 'hellos'. "Gwen is here for an interview."

"You're a new grad?" Carl continued to work quickly and efficiently as he spoke. "Do you have much experience operating?"

"A little," I responded honestly. "I've been doing a little voluntary and locum work in a smallies practice. I've done a few cat spays and castrates, removed a tail and a couple of bitch spays since I graduated."

"Good," Carl sounded pleased and I took that as a good sign. "We do a lot of cat spays and similar surgery."

"Carl does the majority of the operating," Jess confided with a smile. "And Andrew only really does any out of hours under protest. At the moment Alison operates when Carl is on holiday, on call and sometimes during the week."

"You'll get plenty of opportunity and supervision," Carl said. "We're always busy with ops."

It sounded like a good prospect for a baby vet to dip their toe in the surgical waters. I couldn't say I was a particularly enthusiastic surgeon. I enjoyed the occasional op but didn't really have the patience for anything long and involved. Unlike some of my friends, I didn't live to cut.

"Alright," Leah said several minutes later. "On with the tour."

We exited the building via the door opposite the theatre and crossed the small courtyard to another door sheltered by a small roof, requiring a key to open it. After a quick jiggle of the lock and a shunt of the door, Leah managed to coax it open, revealing another office, equally as creatively organised as the other, with more shelving filled with drugs, this time of the large animal variety.

"We keep the meds for farmers over here," Leah observed. "And through there is our x-ray machine."

She indicated a door through which sat a semi-automatic developer, a table and an x-ray unit mounted on a movable metal arm. On one wall was a glass cabinet containing several items of veterinary instrumentation from bygone years. Undoubtedly, they had been considered state of the art at the time, but looking on them as a fresh new graduate, they appeared utterly barbaric to my young eyes.

We left the x-ray room and traversed the courtyard once more to enter through door number three at the end of the 'U' shape formed by the practice and the house attached to it. The house had, at one stage, belonged to the previous owner but had been sold off separately a few decades ago. There had been a vets on site for some eighty years and it had passed through a number of sets of hands before it reached its current owners.

The third of the doors that had befuddled me upon arrival opened onto a set of stairs leading up to a modestly sized flat with an open-plan kitchen-dining-sitting room, a bedroom that also doubled up as further storage and where the lab machines were kept, and a bathroom at the top of the stairs. Two more women; a tall dark-haired girl and a smaller, heavier-set blond were seated at the table, the remains of their lunches strewn between them and *loose women* playing at low volume on the TV.

"We generally use this as our breakroom," Leah informed me after introducing the blond as Clara and the darker girl as another Gwen. "There's a fridge, a microwave and kettle, so all the mod-cons. When we have locums in during staff holidays, they have the option to stay here if they want."

The sound of a car pulling into the courtyard drew Leah to the window overlooking it, making a pleased sound as she glanced through the slightly off-coloured frame.

"Ah, good. Andrew is back. I'll introduce you."

I watched out of the window as a dark blue estate car drove up under the covered area of the yard at Mach speed and jerked to a sharp halt with millimetres to spare between the wall and the headlights. I followed Leah down the stairs, realising as I did they were far steeper than I had initially supposed, and wondering whether a header down them would be a frequent event in my future should I be offered this job. Stairs and I have a somewhat tempestuous relationship, and I have been known to fall down them on a regular basis. Being accident prone was the bane of my existence.

We arrived in the yard just as Andrew erupted from his car. He was a tallish man of indeterminate age, so lean and wiry his frame seemed to have been hewn down to sinew and bone. A thick head of white hair formed an unruly cloud on his head and a matching silver-streaked beard made him look a little like Papa Smurf after a crash diet. His open, friendly features were those of a man who had spent his whole life working in the elements, the remains of a summer tan stubbornly clinging on for dear life.

"Ah!" he said briskly in a very softened Scots accent I recognised from our phone conversation. "You must be Gwen. Sorry I wasn't here when you arrived, farmers won't shut up sometimes."

He glanced across at Leah and started to lead off toward the back door.

"You'll have had the grand tour then, just give me a minute to have a wash and we'll go upstairs for a chat."

A quick wash down of the muck on his hands, arms and face later and I was once again following someone up the stairs to the flat. The girls who had previously been on their lunch had obviously returned to work and we settled on the overstuffed, salmon-pink sofa that immediately attempted to swallow me whole. It was so large I couldn't touch the floor and I wasn't certain I would ever get back out of it.

"So," Andrew pivoted to me, evidently not having the same problem with the sofa. "Alison, our third vet, is leaving to work in 100% equine practice, strange creature that she is, and we're looking for a replacement. We've had a few new grads over the years so we know what kind of support is required; supervised operating and there's always someone available to ask questions about consults or work-ups. We're 50:50 small/large animal practice with some horse work as well, mostly pleasure horses, but there is an eventing stables on the books. We pay Royal College and VDS fees and supply a car and a house in Annfield Plain. We work a 1 in 3 rolling on call rota, and there is some sole charge for Saturday morning surgery. You get a half day off Monday and Friday after a weekend on call and a 4.30 p.m. finish after a night on call."

It was a lot of information to take in at once, and I was silent for a long moment as I digested everything he had said. I opened my trusty red diary and scanned my carefully considered list of interview questions, more for something to do while I thought than because he hadn't covered anything. His no nonsense, straight-to-the-point description of the job had pretty much answered all of my most pressing queries.

"What kind of large animal work do you tend to see here?" I asked, not just for the sake of asking, but because my main interest was in beef suckler cattle. I had done my final year elective in beef cattle and had a genuine enthusiasm for the individual and herd health problems that were part and parcel of keeping and breeding cattle.

"We're mostly beef and sheep now, a lot of our farmers went out of dairy after Foot and Mouth, although we have about four dairies on the books at the moment," he returned quickly and efficiently. "Some of the farmers are stuck in the past, but we have a good number of younger and more forward-thinking farmers who are interested in improving their stock and management practices. Is that something you would be interested in?"

He would know from my CV I had a beef cattle bias, but I was always keen to hold forth on my favourite subject.

"Yes, I'm very interested in beef management strategies and a whole herd approach to improving health and welfare on farm," I happily replied. "It's what I did my final year case studies and journal extracts in. I like sheep and dairy cattle well enough, but my main interest is in the beef side of things."

"And how are you small animal wise? Have you had the opportunity to do much since you graduated? You mentioned voluntary work in your CV?"

"I got bored a couple of months after graduating," I responded ruefully. "I'm not built for sitting at home doing nothing. There's a small animal branch practice not far from home, so I've been going in there a few days a week and doing a little consulting and some non-complicated ops. The vets there have been kind enough to let me stand in on their consults and pick their brains about cases. And in the last couple of weeks one of them has gone off sick so the practice managers offered me some locum work, since they already knew me and it meant they didn't have to pay to place an add or a recruitment agency. It's been really useful. I feel as though I've learned loads since I've been there, and I'm nowhere near as nervous about operating as I was before I started getting stuck in."

"You've been doing mostly spays and castrates then?"

"And a couple of lump removals," I couldn't help my enthusiasm and hoped I wasn't coming off too eager. I really did want to make a good impression. Although the practice was small and a little dated, it seemed like an excellent place to begin a career in truly mixed veterinary work. "I did a tail amputation on a cat last week, which was pretty cool."

"It sounds as though you've been getting some good experience then," Andrew returned. He paused for a moment before continuing. "What are your other interests outside work? Do you belong to any clubs or anything?"

"I do a lot of walking, and I used to do horse riding before uni, and I was part of the rugby club at uni, as well as a couple of self-defense classes. I'm generally pretty active, but I also do a lot of reading. I'm a bit of a literature buff."

Andrew smiled.

"Well, there'll be plenty around here to keep you occupied. There's a decent sized gym in Consett with plenty of exercise classes, and plenty of walks and cycling tracks," he supplied. "Alison plays badminton in Durham on a Thursday night as well."

Great. I couldn't stand to be idle.

Andrew slapped his hands onto his knees and jumped to his feet.

"Right, well, Alison will be back shortly," he said as he led the way back down the stairs and in through the main door. "She's due to see a lame horse at one o'clock, so you can tag along with her if you like and she can show you around the house."

Less than half an hour later a Freelander pulled into the courtyard and a tall, slender woman a few years older than I was jumped out wearing a pair of blue overalls and a war-mask of crimson, or 'claret' as many vets often refer to the odd bit of misplaced blood. She hurried into the practice and immediately began rummaging in the delicate eco-system of the office filing for a pen. Upon her success she quickly whipped out several blood tubes and began to scrawl names and dates upon them.

"Alison, this is Gwen," Andrew affected the introductions, seemingly unconcerned by the manic, almost spaniel-like activity of his employee. "I thought you could take her with you to your next call, and then show her the house."

"Of course," she agreed without pausing the way she bounced around the room gathering lab forms and a biohazard bag to seal the blood tubes into. "Just let me grab a sandwich and then we'll head off."

Thus said, she bounded from the office back toward the door she had entered through, prompting Andrew to call after her;

"And you've got blood on your face!" he grinned at me reassuringly, obviously seeing my slightly shell-shocked expression, having survived the whirlwind that had just been and gone. "She's a great vet, and we're sorry to lose her, but she's mad about horses and there's just not the opportunity to develop that interest with us. Do you have any particular interest in equine practice?"

"Not so that I'd want to go into solely equine practice," I responded perhaps a little too quickly, which again made my prospective employer grin.

Having graduated from Liverpool University, while on rotations at the Philip Leverhulme Equine Hospital – fondly known as the PLEH – I had experienced enough of a busy equine hospital environment to know it was very far down the list of my desired places to work. I didn't mind the odd bit of first opinion horse work, but when we started getting into complicated soft tissue and orthopaedic surgery that's when my attention begins to wander. Give me a cat, a dog, a sheep or a cow any day of the week and I was perfectly content.

"Good!" Andrew rejoined jovially. "Personally, I can't imagine anything worse! I've come to the conclusion she must have a screw loose somewhere, but each to their own I suppose."

Upon Alison's return to the office we chatted as she consumed a truly epic amount of food for a person with such a slender, slight frame, and then we were piling into her Freelander for the short, five-minute journey to the practice accommodation.

It was an old terraced house with concrete cladding and a sadly forlorn square metre of front garden that had been overtaken by some scrubby bushes. It was set back from a relatively busy road, with a lamp post and a bus stop almost directly outside the front door. Compared to the houses on either side, it looked somewhat sad and neglected with its old wooden windows and unkempt appearance. On the inside it was far bigger than I assumed it would be. Downstairs, two large rooms painted a generic magnolia with high ceilings and large windows, one to the front and one to the back, led off the small hall and staircase, directly into the small, rather cramped galley kitchen at the rear of the house. From here a narrow door opened onto a short flight of steps into the back yard, which held a wild perfusion of riotous grasses and a path to the back gate. A garage sat to the back of the kitchen, several stems of buddleia and other weeds growing out of the roof, which leaked during heavy rains. I poked my head inside to find it full of various items of junk, some of which came with the house and some belonged to Alison.

"It's not much good for anything but storing your junk in," she cheerfully informed me. "When they re-did the pavements, they didn't take into account that you'd actually want to open the garage door to get a car in, so now it can't open more than a couple of inches. Not that you'd get a car in there anyway."

Back into the house we went, Alison pointing out various items of furniture that were and were not staying; the floral three-piece suite and the dining room table located in the back room belonged to the house, but the dishwasher and microwave were going with her. I tried to keep a neutral expression on my face at the muddy paw-prints from her rambunctious dog liberally decorating the pale walls and hoped she would do a better job at cleaning than some of my predecessors in various student accommodations over the years.

Up the stairs I peeked into a reasonably sized bathroom with a large shower/bath painted a pleasant blue colour, but with no coverings on the bare wooden boards. The main bedroom faced the front of the house, complete with streetlight almost directly outside the window and a small walk-in alcove with a suspicious amount of black mould on the outside wall and a series of unstable looking shelves against the other. Most of the bedroom furniture was going to a new home, but a large chest of draws almost as tall as me was thankfully staying put. The second bedroom was smaller than the first and looked out over the backyard through a small window that didn't admit much light. Alison seemed to use this room as an office-come-dumping ground for all the stuff without a home elsewhere, and it was currently full of packed and partially packed moving boxes. A large wardrobe belonging to the house took up one corner of the room, and I suspected if I got the job I would use this room for a similar purpose.

Our quicksilver tour completed, I followed her back down the stairs, climbing once again into her 4x4, and off we went to look at a lame horse.

The horse in question lived on a sizable yard about a ten-minute drive from the house in Annfield Plain. We had to negotiate through the busy traffic of nearby Stanley, and as I looked out the window all I saw were modest, greyish buildings that reflected the area's mining history. It wasn't the most picturesque of environs, but since beggars couldn't be choosers, I was willing to overlook its unattractive appearance for the chance of gainful employment.

We arrived at the yard to be greeted by a small crowd of people, horse owners presumably, some seated on plastic garden furniture chatting and smoking, some industriously mucking out stables or grooming their animals. I thought it unusual so many of them would be here on a Wednesday afternoon, seemingly idling the hours away without having any pressing employment to return to. Perhaps I was being judgemental, and it was their day off, but during my work experience in equine practice I had never seen such a large gathering of owners at one time on a weekday.

The horse owners we had come at the behest of quickly identified themselves and the lame horse was led out of its box, grunting and shaking its head in protest at the disturbance to his afternoon nap. It was, indeed, quite noticeably lame on its right fore. Alison spent some time questioning its owners about the length of time it had developed the lameness over, whether it was a fast onset or gradual decline. After discovering it was a relatively rapid onset after being turned out in the field one day and hadn't improved with a number of days of rest and anti-inflammatory medication, Alison began a thorough investigation of the horse's limbs. She began with the sound leg, examining the foot, using hoof-testers to ascertain whether there was any sensitivity in the sole or around the hoof-wall, bending and flexing his joints and palpating the muscle and tendons for any abnormalities. The lame limb received the same careful, methodical inspection, and then she requested the owner trot the horse up on a relatively level, even surface to observe the range of motion and stride of the injured limb.

Several minutes later, as I was having uncomfortable flashbacks of my equine orthopaedics rotations where you would spend hours trotting up horses and being asked whether they were 'sound or lame' and often not being able to tell the difference, Alison pronounced herself satisfied.

"He's definitely more uncomfortable in his lower limb," she pronounced, patting the big animal gently on the shoulder as he came to a snorting stop beside her. "From the flexion tests I'd say it's fetlock related, but to localise it further we'd probably want to perform some nerve blocks, and possibly take some x-rays or ultrasound his tendons to see if there's some other damage involved. Worse-case scenario is he's got a chip fracture or a tear in one of his collateral ligaments."

The owners looked vaguely uncomfortable at the thought of further diagnostic investigation, and the information that the horse was not insured and therefore money might certainly be an issue was quickly solicited. Anything medical involving horses was definitely not cheap, and I wondered quietly why anyone would own such an easily broken animal as this and *not* have at least some form of insurance in case of this eventuality.

"We can certainly continue with box rest and pain-relief," Alison informed them without batting an eyelid and I assumed she was used to this kind of thing happening on a regular basis. "I'll prescribe some *Danilon*; it's a little easier on the stomach than *Bute*, but if we're not seeing significant improvement in the next ten to fourteen days, I would strongly recommend further investigation would be warranted."

A swift rifle around in the boot of her car produced a number of small sachets of powered pain relief to be added to the horse's feed over the next couple of weeks. A prescription was quickly written and handed to the owner with strict instructions regarding the usage of the medication and how much exercise the horse should receive. Once we were back in the car and heading down the drive to the main road, Alison gave a short harrumph.

"They probably won't get it investigated," she sounded more than a little nettled by the prospect. "It's likely nothing, just a bad sprain, or bruising to the tendons and rest will sort it out, but if it's not, I bet they still don't go for referral."

"Oh?" I said curiously.

"Nearly everyone around here seems to have a horse, and the vast majority of them aren't insured," she continued, sounding irked by the information. "And then they wonder why they can't afford to have them treated when something goes wrong."

"That's less than ideal."

We returned to the practice and Alison turned me back over Andrew, before disappearing off to write up her visits for the morning before afternoon consults began. I chatted pleasantly with him and Carl about the background of the practice, and what they were looking for in a vet, for about half an hour further before the interview was over and I was once again heading back to my car.

"It was really nice to meet you," Andrew said pleasantly as we shook hands at the back door of the practice just prior to my departure. "And I hope you enjoyed meeting us all too. We'll be in touch in the next week to let you know our decision. Have a safe journey home."

Five days later my mobile phone rang, caller ID displaying a telephone number I didn't recognise. I answered it with nerves tightening my throat, making my voice sound unlike it usually did; higher and squeakier.

"Hello, Gwen," I recognised Carl's voice and tried to take a few deep breaths, despite the way my diaphragm seemed to be suffering from acute onset paralysis, not helped by the sudden flight of armoured butterflies storming around my stomach. "How are you doing?"

I must have uttered some words that made sense, even though I wasn't certain what I said. I could feel my mother's eyes on me, her expression wary and hopeful at the same time. This phone call had become something of an ordeal in our household, each time a practice phoned I would get my hopes up; only to be let down with the knowledge they didn't want me, necessitating a large consumption of chocolate ice-cream to recover from the disappointment of yet another failure.

I was starting to wonder whether I would ever get a job.

"Well," Carl continued, either not noticing my garbled response, or choosing to overlook it. "I'm calling to say we would like to offer you the job, if you are still available that is."

A startled, high-pitch noise escaped my tightly sealed lips, and I had to bite the inside of my mouth to stop myself from leaping out of my chair and dancing a small jig around the living room. I could hardly believe they were offering me a job. After so many weeks of disappointment I half-wondered whether this was all just a staggeringly real dream.

"Yes!" I managed to just about not squeal the word, forcing myself under some form of regulation so my voice came out vaguely normal, and not like some manic hamster on speed. "Yes, I'm still available. I would love to accept a position at your practice. When would you want me to start?"

I frantically searched for a pen and my trusty red diary to scribble down the information that followed. Alison was finishing in four weeks, meaning the house would be available from the last weekend in March, and I would begin my employment in the first week of April. He promised me an email with all the details and particulars, and once he had put down the phone I shot out of my seat with a loud 'squee-ing' noise that startled the dog out of his bed, and gave into the urge to dance around the room. My mother rapidly joined me, having sussed out the reason for the call, and to anyone looking in through the window we must have looked as though we had completely lost our minds.

I had a job. This was it. I was finally going to become a proper veterinary surgeon.

The rest of my life was about to begin.

CHAPTER FOUR

April

I started working on 2nd April 2012, undertaking the epic task of moving the vast amount of stuff I had managed to acquire the weekend beforehand. With both my Polo and my Mum's Honda Jazz stacked like a very carefully played game of *Tetris*, we navigated the A66 in convoy, a road I was destined to become increasingly familiar with as the months rolled by. We met Carl at the practice early on the Sunday morning to collect the keys to the house and drove the short distance from the village to inspect my new home.

After several moments of battling with the front door lock; the key had a dubious bend midway down the shaft, we spilled into the compact entrance, only to be greeted with the distinct shape of muddy paw-prints on the pale carpet. We exchanged a speaking glance, words unnecessary. It was immediately evident that not even a rudimentary effort to clean had been made before my predecessor vacated the premises.

Muddy paw-prints decorated the walls in the sitting-come-dining room, the less than loved cream carpets smudged with a mixture of dog, dirt and routine traffic. My heart sunk as we viewed the kitchen cupboards, bare save for a thin layer of grime, and I cringed at the thin sheen of pink scum that glowed between the tiles of the shower/bath. The bathmat itself went straight in the bin. It squelched unpleasantly underfoot, a faintly mouldy aroma wafting from it, and I was vaguely uncertain whether, as a veterinary surgeon, having taken an oath and all that, it would be considered unethical to consign this semi-intelligent life-form to landfill.

The state of the house was very similar to that of some student digs I had moved into in the past five years, and I was disappointed I wouldn't have the peaceful Sunday afternoon organising my belongings and psyching myself up for my first day of long-term employment I had hoped for. The whole place would have to be cleaned, practically from top to bottom, before I could bear to unpack any of my things.

"This is disgusting!" Mum tutted, shaking her head at the state the domicile had been left in. "How could you just move out of a house and leave it like this?"

I just silently shook my head, not having an answer for her. Perhaps it was just our particular familial form of obsessive-compulsive disorder, but whenever I had moved out of student accommodation, we always mercilessly blitzed the interior to ensure it was spotless for the next occupants. Regardless of what condition it had been in when we first got there.

Right now, there was work to do.

Unloading my bags, boxes, and perhaps most importantly my Netherland Dwarf house-rabbit from the cars, we made a quick foray to the Tesco, conveniently located just around the corner and raided their household items aisle for suitable cleaning products. Back at the house Mum made a determined effort at the kitchen cabinets while I dug the vacuum cleaner that belonged to the house out of the cupboard under the stairs and attacked the loose detritus adherent to the carpet.

And I discovered exactly why the appliance had obviously been left behind by another of my predecessors.

The suction wasn't great. In fact, it was practically non-existent. I felt as though I was merely pushing the dirt around the floor instead of actually hoovering any of it up. It didn't help that the carpet was apparently hanging on by a thread and I repeatedly had to fish long strands of it from the rotating parts of the hoover head. A new vacuum was evidently going to have to be one of the first things on my list of necessities for my new abode. I would never be able to stand living with the half-hearted effort the current equipment put forth.

Eventually the carpets looked somewhat respectably free of debris, although that didn't mean they looked very much cleaner. A liberal application of carpet cleaner, and another whip around with the by now very asthmatic-sounding hoover, and I was satisfied the flooring looked a lighter shade of dirty-cream than they had before I began. And frankly I was exhausted from lugging the heavy appliance up and down the steep stairs; so it would have to suffice.

After a short lunch break, we started on the walls and bathroom, silently pulling faces at the colour the cloths we were using turned by the time we were finished. It wasn't a large house, but it had taken the best part of the day to get it up to our standards, and by the time Mum and I were satisfied the daylight had already almost completely waned.

"Much better," Mum pronounced as she surveyed the fruits of our labours. The rooms smelled of cleaning products and despite it being a chilly April we had been forced to open the windows in order to air them out a little. "But now I'm going to have to love you and leave you."

Unfortunately, there was no bed in the spare room, and there was absolutely no way I was sharing a room, never mind a bed with my mother. Especially not the night before my new job when I wanted to attempt a good night's sleep.

The last time we had shared a room was on a family holiday nearly three years previously, and neither of us had slept well. Me from having to listen to the cacophonous sound of my mother's snoring, and her from my attempts to silence the noise by intermittently kicking the bottom of her mattress. It had not a particularly restful holiday made.

Needless to say, it was better for everyone involved if she returned

34

to her own home, leaving me to spend the night alone.

I closed the door after seeing her off and wandered somewhat aimlessly around my new home, trailed by Cola the Netherland Dwarf; aka Madam Mim, aka *Sharp pointy teeth* from *Monty Python's Holy Grail*. The rabbit had something of a reputation for being, despite her diminutive size, an unholy terror. She deeply disliked anyone but me, most especially my boyfriend, and had been known to bite, scratch, and chew through other people's electrical cables, and even mug a toddler for a banana. It might have been something to do with me being the all-important hand that feeds, but I was the only person she allowed to do anything with or to her, and I regularly found myself travelling my house with a rabbit on my foot determinedly holding onto the hem of my jeans with her teeth.

A couple of hours later, after organising my uniform for the all-important next day, I reheated the meal I had brought from home and decided on an early night, so I could be bright eyed and bushy tailed for the following morning.

The best laid plans of mice and men…

My alarm woke me on Monday 2nd at an ungodly hour, and I shuffled only semi-alive into the shower, hoping the warm water would kick-start my brain into a semblance of working order. I was neither bright eyed, nor bushy tailed. And even an infusion of caffeine in the form of a strong, bracing cup of tea couldn't seem to shift my mental fog. Some might say a shot of coffee would have been the better choice, but as a recovered coffee addict, finally having kicked my more than ten cups a day habit about three years previously, I tried to avoid the drink as much as possible. It only seemed to send me manic anyway.

The source of my problem was the mattress thoughtfully supplied by my employers. Some people can sleep anywhere, at any time, on anything; my other half once slept in a tent under a bridge in France during a sponsored hitchhike to Morocco. I am unfortunately not one of them. I tend to require complete darkness, silence and a memory foam mattress, none of which my new accommodation possessed. Something told me this situation was going to take some getting used to, and perhaps a significant investment in an orthopaedic mattress before the month was out.

Nevertheless, I scarfed down some breakfast and made my way into the practice, thankful my morning commute lasted for less than five minutes. That first day I was put on light duties, as well as sorting through the gear Alison had removed from her car and deciding what I wanted to carry with me on a day to day basis. Of course, that required me to actually know what I might need on any individual call out, of which I had at that moment no real knowledge. So, erring on the side of caution, I made the executive decision to take it all, and figure out what I would and would not need at some later date.

Thankfully I didn't have to struggle to fit all that kit into the tiny confines of my three-door Polo. Andrew had been in receipt of a new Skoda Octavia Estate company car, meaning I got his older, hand-me-down Skoda, complete with dents, scrapes and the slight aroma of farm. It had been very thoughtfully vacuumed out and cleaned before being turned over for my use, and I spent quite some considerable time puttering around, loading and unloading until I was satisfied with the arrangement of my equipment. It was a distinctly odd feeling, knowing that this car was going to be effectively my office for the foreseeable future. I wanted to make it as comfortable and as convenient for myself as possible but could only really take an educated guess as to what those needs would be.

Despite being only on light duties it was still an incredibly busy day. My poor little newly graduated brain almost exploded with the fast pace of the hectic surgeries; blood samples following vaccines which followed blood glucose testing on an already diagnosed diabetic dog to monitor that the dosage of insulin she was receiving was correct.

It wasn't only small animals that passed in front of me. An ewe that had been lambing for almost twenty-four hours was driven into the yard in the back of a small livestock trailer. As I peered over the edge of the trailer the Mule ewe looked back at me with a mournful, exhausted expression, giving a dispirited bleat as her abdomen contracted, straining without producing more than a thin stream of greenish slime.

"Al-reet, you must be the new lass," the farmer, a Mr Skippool from away up Tow Law, a place I was soon to learn was perhaps the most backward part of the entire country, furrowed his brow as he studied me. I knew exactly what he was thinking… this little girl can't possibly be old enough or strong enough to be farm vet. "Where's Andrew?"

"He's been called out on a calving," I said pleasantly, trying not to let his attitude get to me. It wasn't an uncommon thing to be presented with when you were female and just starting out as a farm vet. "I'm afraid it's only me at the moment."

He grunted something unintelligible

"I suppose ye'll have to do then, flower. It's ring womb, I can't even get a hand in," Mr Skippool propped an arm on the edge of the trailer, peering over at the unfortunate animal within it. "She's been straining for nothing all night. Lamb's likely dead by now, but I'd hoped to save the ewe."

"Alright," I said, pulling on my waterproof leggings and parlour top. "Let me have a feel, and we'll see what we can do."

With the exhausted ewe restrained, I applied a liberal amount of obstetric lubricant to my hand and forearm and carefully inserted my hand into her. Almost immediately I discovered what the farmer had been describing; a tight band of tissue near the cervix preventing the appropriate dilation to occur and the passage of the lamb or lambs into the pelvic canal. The entrance to her womb would barely admit more than three of my fingers, and I have exceptionally small hands in comparison to the average member of the general public.

"You're right," I announced, carefully working my fingers against the tight band of tissue in an attempt to manually dilate the cervix enough to get the lambs out. I wasn't particularly hopeful of success, as she had been in labour for so many hours, and in general if no progress is made within about fifteen to twenty minutes little to no benefit will be achieved. "She's very tight, there's very little room to work inside her. We can try to give her something that might loosen her up a little, and some calcium might help. But there's no guarantee it'll achieve anything."

Some cases of dystocia or aberrations in smooth muscle contraction can be related to inertia caused by a lack of calcium, supplementation of which can help to correct the problems. I didn't really think it would help, but obviously needed to give the farmer a solution to his dilemma.

"If that doesn't help, then I'm afraid we'll have to get the lambs out another way," I continued. "Otherwise you'll probably end up having to shoot the ewe."

"I'd rather not caesar her if that's all the same," the farmer returned gruffly, eyeing me with a hint of suspicion. Obviously as a new graduate my word was not to be trusted in the same manner as a more experienced vet's would. I wondered if he thought I didn't know what I was doing. "Lambs are probably dead, and I'm not sure she's worth it."

I gave him a tight smile and held back my thoughts on the matter. Unfortunately, sometimes what was in the animal's best interest took a backseat to the financial constraints the farming sector was forced to operate under, and if she wasn't going to produce any lambs that year this ewe was a monetary burden. She wouldn't even be worth anything as a cull ewe should he decide to cut his losses, as she was not fit to be sold in her condition, and most definitely not fit for human consumption.

"I'll give it a go."

Fortunately, lambing was something I had plenty of experience with, and was fairly good at.

Giving the smooth muscle relaxant and the calcium injection ten minutes or so to work their magic, I once again applied a liberal dose of lube to my hands and had another feel of the ewe's cervix to see if anything useful might have happened. She felt a little less tight, I could now comfortably fit three fingers into her cervix. Perhaps this might be a more successful enterprise than I had initially assumed.

By the time I had spent about twenty minutes gently working at the tight band of tissue causing all the problems, my wrist and fingers were beginning to cramp, but I had achieved a measure of success. I could now fit my whole hand into the ewe's pelvic canal. I performed a mental fist-pump in celebration, but otherwise kept my exhilaration from appearing on my face. Undoubtedly the farmer would think my excitement a sign of my inexperience.

Another squirt of the thick, gloopy lube and I managed to advance my forearm far enough to get a good grasp on her lamb. I stuck my little finger up the lamb's nose, checking to see if there were any signs of life, but the baby showed no response to my manhandling, exactly as I had expected. Arranging forelimbs and head in a position resembling a swan-dive, I slipped a plastic-coated wire lambing snare around the back of the lamb's ears, securing it tightly in the mouth, applying gentle traction to the legs and guiding the head along with it. The lamb engaged in the pelvic canal and I mentally crossed my fingers and pulled a little bit harder. For a moment or two I thought it wasn't going to come, and despite all my effort and patience I would still have to either caesar the ewe or put her down.

Then, just as I was about to give it up as a lost cause, something gave and the lamb slid smoothly out into the world. On closer inspection it was, indeed, dead. Its fleece was stained a dirty yellow with faecal material, its little tongue swollen and blue. Often when a lamb was distressed during lambing, or just about to die, it would pass the meconium; the first faeces passed by any mammalian infant. The lamb *had* been alive, but evidently the long labour and the ring womb had killed it.

It wasn't a particularly large lamb, which was unusual if it was a single, so I applied another coating of lube and delved back inside to check if the lamb had a sibling. I was unsurprised to encounter another lamb. This one came easier than the first and was also no longer with us. There was no third.

I injected the ewe with some anti-inflammatory pain-relief – off license in sheep, but there were very few medications that *were* licensed for use in that particular species – some antibiotics and a further jab of calcium and the farmer took her home. He was happy, the ewe was alive, and I'd successfully performed my first farm animal procedure as a qualified veterinary surgeon. Perhaps he would trust me a little more the next time I was called upon to minister to his stock.

And that was not the last large animal intervention I had to make that day. Shortly after the ewe left, we received a phone call informing us another farmer was coming down with a lamb requiring its umbilicus tying off to prevent it from herniating its intestinal tract through the incomplete section of the body wall. Then not long after *that* patient had left another lamb was brought into the practice with a fracture of the tibia and fibula of the right hind limb. As it was a small lamb, and fixating the fracture was a relatively simple procedure, the application of a small green gutter splint and a half Robert-Jone's bandage and the little lamb was almost immediately hobbling around on its make-shift limb.

A job well done. I felt a sense of relieved achievement. I could vet successfully. I could do the farm work I had been presented with thus far.

It was, in fact, a *huge* relief.

My first full day of work passed more rapidly than I thought it would, and before I knew what was happening, I was returning home in my Polo in order to park it up outside the house, effectively retiring my little car from active service. On the next day Leah would be picking me up on the way into work so I would be able to collect the Skoda and have it available should it be required. That night I collapsed onto my less than comfortable mattress, utterly exhausted, and slept the sleep of the dead for the next twelve hours.

It was startlingly tiring being a fully-fledged vet.

My second day of work was also my first night of on call.

The day had passed with similar vigour as the one previous. A veritable bevy of vaccinations and other rudimentary consultations hurtled in my direction almost as soon as I had set foot over the threshold of the practice, thankfully none of them too taxing for my poor, befuddled, newly graduated brain.

After an hour of small animal surgery, Andrew and I were jettisoned from the practice to see to our various large animal visits, while Carl got his teeth into the arm-length list of surgical procedures awaiting his attention. My first solo horse vaccination under my belt, without any damage to life and limb from the notoriously flighty creature, I breezed through two more ewes in need of medication; one suffering from pneumonia, a relatively common occurrence at that time of the year, the other a mother-to-be with pregnancy toxaemia.

This particular condition is a common one of late gestation, typically characterised by partial anorexia and a dull or lethargic mental state, often with neurological signs. If left untreated it can prove fatal. It is most commonly seen in animals carrying two or more foetuses and is primarily due to inadequate dietary intake of nutrition. The toxaemia is generally treated with the oral administration of glucose and electrolytes along with other vitamin supplements. Unfortunately, it was often necessary to abort the pregnancy to save the ewe as she wouldn't be able to withstand the energy requirements of the remainder of her gestation.

The successful application of a stomach tube and drenching of the problematic sheep without drowning the ewe, or destroying the rubber tube, was celebrated with a half-past-four Mars bar and a happy buzz of pride. It might seem an unusual and unlikely achievement to be proud of, but it was no mean feat. It was often the case that the animal chewed the tube if a gag wasn't placed correctly, and I had heard several horror stories of my peers passing stomach tubes, pumping several litres of fluid supposedly into the rumen in an attempt to correct a dehydration, only to discover after the animal had died after most of the fluid had ended up in the lungs.

Thankfully that night the capricious and often vengeful gods of on call decided to take pity upon me; the on-call practice mobile didn't ring once. Of course, that didn't stop me from waking up every couple of hours over night to check it hadn't rung, or it had signal.

For most new grads, on call was something that was a struggle to get used to. And I even knew some very experienced vets who had moments of panic when the phone or pager failed to disturb them during a period of on call. It isn't uncommon for someone, when their on-call pagers remained eerily silent, to call the pager company just to make sure it was actually working.

A disturbed night of sleep later and I happily returned both the phone and the caesar kit to their homes in the practice.

Over the next few days I began to see some more complicated small animal cases and received my first general practice introduction to a condition capable of striking fear into the hearts of horse owners up and down the country; colic.

Having graduated from Liverpool, I had seen more than my fair share of colic surgeries and done enough four in the morning colic checks to be able to do them in my sleep. I remember one particular gruelling night on my out-of-hours equine rotation when we had four horses requiring surgery arrive one after the other throughout the night. I was, and still am, in awe of the operating clinician on call that night. An older professor, who had pioneered abdominal surgery in equines since the 1970s, he had a conveyor-belt system in place whereby as one horse was coming around from anaesthesia in the recovery box at the far end of the equine operating theatre, another was simultaneously being knocked down in preparation for surgery. The man was like a machine. I have no idea how he managed four surgical colics in one night and wasn't – or at least didn't appear to be – completely exhausted and physically broken by the end of it. I was a reasonably fit twenty-two-year-old, and yet by the time the morning came I felt as though I was ninety.

Of course, colic isn't exactly a condition per se. The term merely refers to abdominal pain, and is actually a clinical sign, rather than a diagnosis. It is a catch-all description encompassing all forms of gastrointestinal conditions causing pain, as well as other causes of abdominal pain not involving the gastrointestinal tract.

My first encounter with the frontline diagnosis of a colicking horse came in the form of a twenty-year-old Shetland pony called Rufus who, despite being quite severely unwell, wasn't particularly sold on any kind of veterinary intervention.

Shetland ponies, notwithstanding their diminutive stature, are often far more difficult to minister to than their larger compatriots. They seem to suffer from a sufficiency of character, and a determination to be as awkward as physically possible. They will kick, bite, shove and on occasion head-butt in an attempt to get their own way, even if it is intrinsically detrimental to their continuing existence.

Rufus was a perfect example of his breed. A light chestnut in colour, he was a hairy, opinionated, obstinate little beast. Even though he was thin – a novelty when dealing with Shetlands as they are often relatively obese – with foul-smelling diarrhoea, a very low temperature and impressively elevated heartrate, he had apparently made it his mission in life to make my job as difficult as possible.

Obviously, in any case such as this, a thorough clinical examination of the patient was incredibly important in order to be certain no physical symptom was being overlooked. However, that was often easier said than done. It was relatively difficult to perform an examination as Rufus ducked, weaved, bobbed and barged about the yard, dragging his hapless owner along with him.

"I d'know *what* you're playing at, man!" Mrs Kirkcaldy; an older, rail-thin woman, chirped in distress as her beloved pony unceremoniously towed her from one end of the yard to the other as I trailed him with a stethoscope trying to listen to heart or lungs or gut noises. "He's normally quiet, like! Ha'way man, Rufus, will ya just stand still."

I just about bit back my disbelieving snort. I had never met a Shetland who knew *how* to behave. There was a reason this breed had a particular nickname - a variation of their name, but with a single letter replacement – among those of my profession.

"I'm sure he's just uncomfortable, Mrs Kirkcaldy," I returned in a placatory tone, deciding discretion was the better part of valour. I had experienced enough horse owners in my short career to understand they were a breed all to their own. It was a pointless exercise to attempt to contradict them about the temperament of their precious animals.

Nearly fifteen minutes later, Rufus, in his unwell state, had sufficiently tired himself out by his exertions to allow me to get a reasonable idea of his physical parameters. He was truly a very poorly little pony, not that it was visible in his attitude. I decided to draw some blood to check his problems weren't due to a deeper seated dysfunction than an upset gut, and provide some anti-inflammatory pain relief as well as some anti-spasmodic medication to help with the diarrhoea, which is when I discovered the second difficulty in administering to Shetland ponies.

Their necks are incredibly short, impossibly muscular and impenetrably hairy. Anatomically, I knew where to expect to find the jugular vein. Unfortunately, Rufus seemed to have hidden his somewhere completely different. You wouldn't expect it to be too hard to hit a vein the width of my finger, but that is where you'd be wrong. Taking blood from a Shetland pony is an art-form, and one that, at that stage of my career, I had yet to master.

Eventually I managed to locate his hidden vein, although only after being stomped, shoved and head-butted hard enough to make my eyes cross. Drawing enough blood to fill three vials containing different preservative media I injected the pain-relief and just about stopped myself from breaking into the hallelujah chorus when finally the ordeal was over.

Until the next day, when I had arranged to re-visit the patient, hopefully to find him significantly improved.

When I at last returned to the welcoming shelter of the practice, Andrew was chomping into a large sandwich overflowing with meat and vegetables as Carl practically inhaled a cream-cake the size of his forearm. Upon seeing me they both immediately stopped what they were doing and stared with a degree of concern emanating from their persons.

"Are you alright, Gwen?" Andrew queried, a frown furrowing his fuzzy silver brows until they practically touched his nose.

"Yes," I replied, confused by the way Jess, who had just joined us, was also frowning at me. It was only a little white lie; I had a headache and was starving; one likely the cause of the other. "Why?"

Rather than replying Jess pulled a compact mirror from her bag and showed me my reflection. And then I understood why they all looked a little worried.

My face was paler than usual beneath a thin layer of dirt, likely transferred to me during my wrestling match with the pony. But perhaps the most pressing problem was the nice, livid bruise currently blossoming around my left eye.

"Rufus head-butted me," the words kindled the fires of understanding in each of their expressions.

Jess pulled a small moue of sympathy and patted me on the shoulder.

"Cake?" Carl gestured toward the remaining pastry in a bakery box on the windowsill, obviously of the opinion, as were the majority of vets in the world, that sugary treats were the answer to all life's problems.

Even after only a few days of working there, everyone had discovered I had a rather serious sweet tooth and a tendency to turn into the incredible hulk when my blood-sugar got too low.

"Go have lunch and a sit-down," Andrew instructed as I helped myself to the offered delicacy. "You'll feel better once you've had something to eat and the chance to get off your feet. Do you have a headache?"

"A bit," I returned a little reluctantly. I didn't really like being made a fuss of. "But I'm hungry, and it just feels like a normal hangry headache."

"Alright," he allowed, his frown easing only a small amount. "But if you start to feel dizzy or unsteady let someone know."

I threw him a salute and took my treat upstairs to demolish my lunch to the accompaniment of *Loose Women*.

The next day I went back to see Rufus once again, armed with his blood work-up, which was thankfully all within the normal parameters. Mrs Kirkcaldy beamed at me as I opened my car door, her lined features immediately changing from delighted to worried as she evidently clocked the shiner that had only become more livid overnight. I was only relieved I didn't have concussion.

"Are you al-reet, pet? You've had a reet clatter!" she trilled, her voice a lilting, softened Geordie accent clucking in a grandmotherly fashion over my first war wound of first opinion practice. Not the first bruise, or even the worst, I had received while vetting, but the only one I'd been paid for acquiring. "You bad lad, Rufus! Look what you've done to the nice vet lady!"

She shook her finger in admonishment at the pony who looked remarkably unmoved by the chastisement as he munched unconcerned on the contents of the hay-net hanging in front of him.

"How's he doing this morning, Mrs Kirkcaldy?" I queried, wanting to quickly move on from the subject of my black eye. "He certainly seems a bit perkier today than yesterday."

"Why aye, he's back to his old self," she beamed at me once again. "His muck was almost solid when I skipped out this morning, and he's been eatin' his head off!"

"Excellent," I couldn't help but smile at the bubbly, jubilant lady. "Well, shall we try to have another look at him?"

As expected, Rufus didn't cooperate, but his parameters when I did eventually manage to take them were better than the previous day. His heart rate was markedly lower, proving it had likely been pain related yesterday. His guts were moving at much more normal pace as well, the impressive recovery he had made pleasing me immensely. And not just for the fact I wouldn't have to try to hit a vein a second time.

"Excellent," I repeated. "I'm much happier with him today, and his blood results came back pretty much normal, so there's not much to be concerned about there. I think we'll keep him on some pain-relief for another few days, and if the diarrhoea still hasn't settled down, I'll get you to bring us a sample to send away for testing."

I produced the appropriate sachets to add to his feed from the boot of my car and provided her with written instructions as to its dosage. Then we parted ways, both pleased it hadn't been anything more serious than a simple gut upset.

For my first encounter with the notoriously difficult colic, it could have been much worse.

CHAPTER FIVE

April – Weekends are supposed to be relaxing

My on-call weekend rota began Friday night and finished Monday morning when everyone else turned up for work. My first of these happened after my first very busy week of work.

Friday night surgery finished late – not an unexpected happening in a vet practice with as fast a pace and as many clients as Oakbank – in a large part due to the dubious charms of a Rottweiler cross Doberman named Gripper.

Gripper was a farm guard dog belonging to one of the practice's less than jovial clients, who frankly, to this day, terrified me. Mr Parkfield was a large man; well over six feet tall, and broad enough that his presence seemed to fill the entire, admittedly diminutive, waiting room, possessing a nose with a diverted septum, having been broken one too many times in the past. His general attitude was a whisker shy of obnoxious, and I later learned he had once been on trial for attempted murder – only his intended victim miraculously withdrew his testimony only days before the court date, leaving the Crown Prosecution Service with no legal leg to stand on. Andrew's favourite joke was that he should employ the services of Mr Parkfield and his father to sort out the laundry-list of the practice's bad debtors. A couple of broken kneecaps into the deal and he would never have a problem with toxic debt ever again.

None of which knowledge particularly helped *me* as I stood

behind the table in my consulting room and hoped I wasn't staring at my latest patient with the same expression a juicy mouse did the cat about to eat it.

"Now then, Henny," Mr Parkfield practically barked across the table at me, both his, and his dog's, ginormous size making me feel like a child.

Despite having only been at the practice – and indeed in the North East – for a sum total of a week, I had already seemed to have acquired a list of pet-names as long as my arm. Initially I had thought about taking offence to the generally patronising tone they were said in; I wasn't a petal or a flower or a henny – whatever that might actually *be* – but I had thought better of it. I had bigger bridges to cross with some of the clients than what they wanted to call me, and to be honest I wasn't sure I had the energy to spare.

"He's gone and et rat-bait, the stupid bugger," Mr Parkfield continued and I wondered whether he had ever learned to use his 'inside' voice, or if he just did it to be intimidating.

I took a deep breath and forced myself to put my personal feelings of trepidation aside. Mr Parkfield was a client, just like any other, and as terrifying as both dog and owner appeared, they needed *my* professional expertise.

"Do you know how long ago he ate the rat poison, or what the product is called?" I asked, hoping my voice didn't let on how nervous I really was.

I knew exactly what I needed to do in this situation, but I wasn't particularly looking forward to the inevitable clinical examination of my patient. Gripper wasn't precisely *growling* at me, even though I was all the way across the room, but he was regarding me with that typical guard-dog expression that advised; *"come any closer and I'll rip your face off."*

"About a half-hour ago," Mr Parkfield supplied. "Saw him doin' it but couldn't get it off him in time. I've got the label."

Gripper, I discovered once I had more thoroughly perused his clinical notes, seemed to have a taste for rat-poison. This was not the first time he had been to the practice for this sort of thing and I was at least glad his owner knew the drill by now, if not slightly bemused why he didn't make sure the dog could no longer get at the chemicals.

"Right, well, that makes life a little easier," I breathed a sigh of relief. "All we need to do if he's not showing any clinical signs is make him sick, and cover him for a few days with some vitamin K. Although it would probably be a good idea to take some bloods in a week to check it's not interfered with his clotting factors."

I took another deep breath and mentally girded my loins for the ordeal to come. "Let's have a look at him then. Does he need a muzzle while I examine him?"

Mr Parkfield laughed.

"Nah," he said dismissively. "He's as soft as butter. You wouldn't bite anyone, would ya, son?"

Gripper looked at me with a deep sense of suspicion I was in no position to allay. I tried to keep the doubts off my face. I had learned during my small animal rotations in final year that a good poker-face was an essential skill for anyone entering the veterinary profession. You wouldn't believe some of the things that come out of client's mouths. I wasn't inclined to believe Mr Parkfield, but at least he got a good grip on the dog's collar and nose when I approached stethoscope and thermometer in hand.

The majority of rat poisons contain a derivative of the anticoagulant drug Warfarin. This drug interferes with the body's ability to produce vitamin K dependent clotting factors, and certain other proteins important in the regulation of normal anti-bleeding mechanisms. Dogs who have ingested rat poison show a variety of different clinical signs, depending on the length of time between consumption and when the animal is presented for treatment. In very advanced cases, lethargy, difficulty breathing, pale gums and a slower than normal heart rate. Some will suffer from nosebleeds and vomit blood.

Thankfully, Gripper was exhibiting none of these presenting signs. With only half an hour since he'd eaten the poison there had been little time for the chemicals to enter his system and cause problems.

His growl and stiff stance when I crouched at his side to begin my examination had my nerves jangling uncomfortably, and I made sure I kept a careful eye on his expression and movement throughout the time it took for me to complete my tasks. As much as many owners say they can control their animals, it is a statement I have learned to be greatly wary of. I like all my fingers and features exactly where they are. Ideally, I should have put a muzzle on the dog, regardless of Mr Parkfield's confidence, but I have also learned when to pick my battles, and I suspected getting a muzzle on Gripper would have been a fight in and of itself.

Once I was finished, all parameters normal, gums nicely pink and moist, I jumped to my feet with perhaps undue haste, as Mr Parkfield had been true to his word and the dog hadn't tried to eat me. I retreated back to my computer, masterfully ignoring the sardonic smile on my client's pugnacious features, just glad to be out of the danger zone.

"If you'd just follow me, we'll pop Gripper on the scales to get an accurate weight to work out what drugs he needs."

Normally we didn't encourage clients to venture into the back portions of the practice; the prep/kennel room where the scales lived, just in case we were operating or restraining a particularly difficult patient, but there was no way I was going to manage that beast of a dog all by myself. Weighing complete, I returned Mr Parkfield to my consulting room and made my excuses to go and hide in the sanctuary of the dispensary to ferret through the books kept on a far too high shelf in search of The Book of All Knowledge. This sacred tomb was also known as *The BSAVA Small Animal Formulary*, and it contained the dosages of almost all medications routinely used in practice. I rapidly looked up the dose of apomorphine; a drug derivative of morphine and a dopamine receptor antagonist that in humans is used in the treatment of Parkinson's disease, but in dogs is mainly used to induce vomiting, as well as both the injectable and tablet dosage of vitamin K.

Returning to Gripper with my collection of needles and tablets, I explained my plans to his owner. Injecting the apomorphine under the skin, as there was no way I was trying to go intravenously in *this* dog, we quickly removed to the large drain at the edge of the carpark. Making a dog vomit is a distinctly messy and disgusting procedure, and best done in an area easily hosed down.

After waiting for some movement for approximately ten minutes, I finally saw Gripper starting to lip-smack, looking decidedly uncomfortable, as his eyes widened in an expression of panic. Several dry heaves followed and then a copious quantity of drool flowed from his chops. Gripper's abdomen contracted in a series of hard, rough pulses as a vile volcano of combined dogfood and small blue packets spewed from his mouth, predictably missing the drain by a good several feet. If you think dog-meat is off-putting in its original form, then it is disgusting to the nth degree the second time around. The smell of warm dog food, mixed with bile and the sound of violent retching, is and of itself vomit-inducing. Unfortunately, I have a particular weakness; watching someone, or something, else being sick invariably makes me want to heave up the contents of my own stomach. So, I stood some distance apart from man and dog, waiting for the torrent of vomit to cease.

However, true to form, Gripper was anything but a textbook case. Apomorphine generally lasts for approximately thirty minutes, guaranteeing that the unwanted items or food is evacuated from the stomach, but without risking dehydration from the act of vomiting itself. Almost an hour later, after the sun had nearly completely disappeared from the sky and the sharp April air began to nip at my face and hands, poor Gripper was still going. By now he was producing little more than a thin stream of bile and mucous, his flanks heaving with the effort and his eyes red with the strain. His

THEY NEVER TOLD ME THAT AT VET SCHOOL

face was a picture of abject misery, every time he glanced in my direction an expression of dejected accusation flitting over his cross Rottie features.

I felt really sorry for him. As much as it was a necessity to get all the remaining pieces of rat-poison out of his system, it was a horrible experience to spend so long being sick. Popping back into the practice I drew up some injections of an anti-emetic and anti-inflammatory pain relief to administer, and twenty minutes later once the dry heaves had ceased, Mr Parkfield took his dog and vitamin K tablets home, giving me a quick, approving nod as he departed.

As we were shutting down computers and locking up the practice, Jess gave my shoulder a quick, supportive squeeze.

"You did a good job," she told me just before we both got into our cars. "Mr Parkfield is a difficult one to please at the best of times. He seemed pretty happy with what you did tonight, and that's an achievement!"

Saying our goodbyes, knowing we would meet again bright and early the following morning, I trundled up the hill to my house, stumbling in through the door and scraping together a hasty evening meal to bolt down, burning my mouth in the process. Most people who do any kind of on call work inevitably learn to eat quickly. It might be superstition, but you were never more likely to be called out than when you were trying to eat your dinner.

After my meal I sagged onto the floral couch to watch some TV, a small brown rabbit perched on my knee, determinedly avoiding any attempt I made to stroke her. Despite my levels of fatigue and the lateness of the hour, I was loath to make the trip upstairs to my uncomfortable bed. I didn't want the hassle of getting undressed, getting all warm and snuggly under my duvet, only to have to go back out to minister to some sheep or cow or sick small animal. In general, the majority of farmers do a last check on their stock around eleven o'clock in the evening, routinely calling for any veterinary assistance half an hour to an hour after that. Pet owners sometimes called about that time of night, having been looking at their sick pet for the best part of the evening, and deciding that no, they could not leave the animal until the morning.

Thankfully the only excitement to occur on that Friday night was a phone call from my boyfriend – who had been on a three-month Erasmus project in Helsinki, Finland, to announce he was back in the country for good.

Saturday morning had me coasting into the practice at quarter to nine for Saturday surgery. In an attempt to be kind, Andrew and Carl had blocked off several of the available appointments meaning I only had a few boosters and vomiting and diarrhoea dogs to work my way through on my first sole-charge surgery. I was grateful and relieved by their foresight. Although these were not particularly difficult consultations in and of themselves, the rigors of ten-minute slots and the uncertainties of being very new to the game, made it a chore to keep to time. Eventually I would look back at these early days and wonder why it all seemed so hard, but then it was a very stressful challenge.

After surgery finished, Jess sent me out to Highsweep Livery Stables to see a lame horse. With dread in my heart, as I couldn't say equines were my favourite animal to vet, I headed out to the yard. Although I was in possession of detailed directions, I still managed to get lost, driving past the entrance to the concrete slab paved track four times, before I saw the small, off-coloured name plate advertising the name of the yard that was obscured by an exuberant woody shrub. I bumped and bounced my way along the half-mile track to enter through an impressive pair of gateposts to a clean, tidy yard containing several well-built, well-cared for stable buildings.

Taking a deep breath, I tried to settle the deep flutter of butterflies that took flight in my stomach. A lame horse could be either very simple, or impossibly complicated, and I couldn't help the nagging doubt in the back of my mind that I was about to bite off more than I could chew.

I met the owner of the horse as she emerged from one of the buildings, a woman who was several years older than me with a pleasant open expression on her face. We greeted each other and I followed her into the dimly lit stable-block, along a wide, swept-clean corridor with sturdily constructed stables on either side. Several large horsey heads poked over their stable doors as we passed. Some nickering and whiffling in search of a scratch or a treat ensuing.

My patient inhabited the last stable in this particular block. The big, gorgeous, bay animal was standing with his rear toward the door, his head lowered almost to the rubber matted floor with his hip cocked resting his right hind foot. The lines of his body screamed dejection with every discontented, huffed exhale, and despite our arrival, and the curiosity of his companions, he didn't even cock an ear toward us. His owner entered the stable, slipping on a head-collar and gently shoved his massive hindquarters away from the door so I could cross the threshold without the danger of being booted should he take offence to my presence. One could never be too careful with horses, even if they were currently on three legs. As has been said by many a famous person; *horses are dangerous at both ends and uncomfortable in the middle.*

Slipping into the stall, I completed a visual and physical examination of the normal limb, figuring out what was *normal* for this particular patient before I took a look at the problem leg. On inspection the limb seemed rather uninteresting. There was no particular abnormality I could find, until I got out my trusty hoof-testers. Using this pair of pincers on steroids I carefully tested all around the sole of the horse's foot for soft areas or sensitivity that would indicate a bruise, or damage to the lower surface of the hoof, which might uncover the potentially complicated source of the problem.

As I put my testers across the seat of corn on the inside of the hoof they sank into the sole and the horse tried to jerk his foot away, making my heart hammer out a machine-gun burst of rapid beats at the thought of being kicked. A corn is a bruise formed between the sensitive and insensitive layers of the sole of the foot. The 'seat of corn' is the most commonly affected area, located between the hoof bar — a continuation of the hoof wall that extends toward the heel approximately halfway along the frog — and the wall, near the heel. A corn does not always cause a horse to be lame, and if they do, the lameness is usually not severe.

In this case the horse was what we would call 'hopping lame', meaning he was unwilling to bear any weight on that foot. I suspected the problem was a little bit more than a simple corn. Returning to the car for a pair of hoof-knives, I once again placed the foot gripped between my knees, in classic farrier stance, and had an experimental dig at the area of softened, sore sole that was the root of our problems.

At first, I was very tentative in the slivers of sole I removed from the foot, little more than surface scrapes that did neither me nor the horse any good. It was an effort to appear calm and professional under the beady eyes of an owner who had no idea who I was, or even whether I was competent enough to perform such a procedure on their precious animal. I'd never done anything like this on a horse before. Sure, I had *watched* it done on various equines, and I'd pared enough of cattle and sheep feet to at least have an idea of how to hold the knife, but there is a world of difference between a cow and a horse. I could almost feel my heart beating in my bone-dry mouth, hoping I didn't completely foul this task up and do more harm than good. In any rural or horsey community gossip spreads fast and I didn't want to become *that new vet who can't trim a horse's foot*.

Come on Gwen, I gave myself a mental slap as I was in danger of sliding down a spiral of self-doubt and uncertainty I would never recover from. *Put on your big girl pants and get the job done!*

A deep breath, and a bolder, more confident stroke of the knife had a twenty-pence piece sized chunk of hoof detaching from the harder sole surrounding it, a rush of smelly, greyish fluid rapidly following the piece of hoof. An even greater flood of relief swept through my body, and I had to concentrate hard to not hyperventilate with a giddy sense of achievement and triumph.

As I had suspected; it was a foot abscess.

Horse foot abscess generally have a fairly classical presentation; a horse gone suddenly lame, more often on the rear than on the front feet. The horses also have a habit of waving the foot at you, whether because it stung, or some other reason, but thankfully they weren't too difficult to treat. Relieving the pressure tended to be the best resolution, but also applying a poultice to the foot to draw out any remaining infection helped to prevent a reoccurrence of the issue. Antibiotics were most certainly *not* to be used.

As a Liverpool graduate I had quite a bit of experience bandaging horses' feet. After making my hole a little larger to aid in the draining of the discharge, I pressed a damp iodine-soaked poultice to the sole of the foot, and fell back upon the comfortingly familiar routine of wrapping the whole thing in layers of bandages that was almost like a security blanket. I had done it so many times, bandaging a foot was something I could do without having to think, allowing the adrenaline high of my success to crash and fade from my system, leaving my hands noticeably trembling.

Retrieving a roll of black, heavy-duty duck-tape from my supplies I cut off several strips, layering them into a criss-cross pattern until they formed a 20x20cm square. Placing the foot in the middle I contoured the edges around the hoof, wrapping several more strips of tape around the top to keep it on. This particular use of duck-tape was a mark of having graduated from Liverpool Veterinary School, and once again something useful and practical I could do in my sleep that would hopefully seem very professional and efficient to the owner.

An injection of pain-relief, an exchange of pain-relieving sachets, and we were done.

"Leave the poultice on for at least a couple of days if you can," I instructed as the client walked me back to my car. "He's a quiet enough lad, so I think he should tolerate it fairly well. If it's still producing gunk when the poultice is removed you can either put another one on or leave it open and stick his foot in a bucket of Epsom Salts. Any trouble, just give us a shout and we'll come out and have another look."

I pulled out of the yard and drove halfway down the track before I was no longer visible to anyone standing by the buildings. Stopping the car, I put my head onto the steering wheel and took several deep, calming breaths, trying to repress the urge to shout my triumphant success at the top of my lungs. And failed.

"Yes!" I yelled, the sound of my voice filling the interior of the car as I fist-pumped and high-fived the air, probably grinning like a complete maniac.

It felt *so good* to have achieved. So good to leave a happy horse and client and know they wouldn't, couldn't, have anything bad to say about me.

My clinical, academic knowledge was good, even if I did say so myself, but being a vet in the real world was much more stressful than the safe, insulated environment of a university hospital, or even the university first opinion practice. Before there had always been someone to ask, someone to tell me what I *should* be doing, or to at least bounce ideas off if I wasn't 100% certain what was wrong with the animal. Out here I was all on my own, face to face with the owner who expected me to have an answer. I couldn't just ask them to hang on a moment while I phoned a friend.

It was definitely all a lot scarier than it seemed.

Upon my return to the practice I found a client with a rather poorly dog awaiting my arrival.

The dog was of indeterminate breeding, relatively elderly and miserably collapsed in the waiting room. The owners were in bits; a middle-aged couple visibly distressed by the condition of their beloved pet. After struggling to get the dog, a rather lovely old man called Buster, who was something of a dead-weight into the consult room, we laid him on the floor, as getting him onto the table seemed to be a bridge too far. After a quick scan of his clinical history, revealing a chronic kidney condition, I dropped to my knees and performed a quick, but thorough examination. Unfortunately for Buster he was not in a good way. His gums were pale, his heart bounding in a rapid beat I could barely count, accompanied by a murmur loud enough I could hear it with my stethoscope not even touching his chest wall.

My heart sank like a stone and lodged as a heavy weight somewhere in the vicinity of my stomach.

Considering we had no documented history of heart disease this was a very bad sign.

I palpated his grossly distended belly, feeling a squishy, fluid consistency called a fluid thrill, which made a disconcerting 'sloshing' sound when I placed my stethoscope on his abdomen. An urgent sensation of extreme unease shot up my spine and I felt my heartrate pick up almost instantaneously.

Immediately a screaming list of differentials scrolled across the inside of my skull, like the green on black letters and numbers from *The Matrix*, none of them staying in one place long enough for me to consider whether they were correct or not. Was it a transudate, exudate, blood, peritonitis… was it definitely related to the obvious heart failure, or was he suffering from liver disease as well, or a tumour? Did he have a tumour in his spleen that had burst and was haemorrhaging into his abdomen? Was it related to the already noted kidney disease? Had he developed pyelonephritis leading to a protein-losing nephropathy, or was it gut related instead? Could it be a protein-losing enteropathy causing fluid to follow the protein from his gastrointestinal tract down an osmotic gradient into his abdomen?

Were the heart failure and the chronic kidney disease related? Loss of blood pressure due to lack of kidney function could lead to a feedback loop in the body that flogged the heart, forcing it to beat faster and faster in an attempt to retain pressure through the kidney filtration system. The heart, a failing pump, would struggle to keep up with demand, leaky valves causing the loud murmur sounds due to turbulence and backflow of blood into the overstretched chambers of the heart.

By this time, I was beginning to hyperventilate. The stress of the situation, of correctly diagnosing the problem, of the teary, judgemental eyes of the owners, of doing what was right for the animal, was starting to get to me. My mouth was dry and I could feel my ears burning. A strange prickling sensation fizzed at the backs of my eyes and I knew I was close to becoming overwhelmed by the situation.

Come on, Gwen, I gave myself a good mental shake, hoping it would snap me out of this sudden rushing freight-train of panic bearing down upon me. *You've got this. You can do this. You can figure this out.*

I pulled my stethoscope from my ears, the pretence of needing the quiet to listen to his chest and abdomen had given me enough breathing room to get myself into some semblance of 'together'. I was a responsible, qualified professional. I had this…

So why did I feel like such a fraud?

I felt like at any moment there should be an actual *real* vet stepping in to take over the difficult parts of this conversation. But there wasn't anyone else. I was the only one available and I felt like such an imposter.

"He's a very sick old man," I began, hearing the unnatural squeak in my voice and trying to clear my throat in an attempt to sound in some way vaguely normal, and not as though I wanted to run away as far and as fast as physically possible. "He's developed a rather significant heart murmur since the last time we saw him, and it's likely the swelling of his abdomen is ascites due to congestion of blood back through his liver. It's all probably related to his kidney problems, and he's just fallen over the edge of what his body can cope with. To be completely certain we'd have to pop a needle into his abdomen and draw off some fluid, and take bloods…" I really wasn't looking forward to doing either of those things. I'd never performed a peritoneal tap before, and the thought of trying to draw blood from a dog in such serious cardiovascular distress was enough to give me nightmares... "But I think we have to seriously consider whether it would be fair to Buster to put him through anything further."

"If it is heart failure," Mrs Blakely said softly, her voice cracked and scratchy with tears. "Is there anything we could do for him?"

"There are some medications we could try him on," I returned uncomfortably. I wasn't sure this dog was within the reach of medical intervention. With such a loud, severe murmur to have occurred in such a short span of time, plus the large volume of ascites I was doubtful Buster would cope with *anything*. "We could try to get rid of the fluid on his belly and give him something to help his heart beat more efficiently, but there is no guarantee that it will improve his current condition. You might find we give him medications, and nothing changes. You might find we've put him through another twenty-four hours of struggling to breathe and move for nothing. I-I think we need to consider that there might not be anything we *can* do for him, and it might be time to say that enough is enough and put him to sleep. We have to do what is in *his* best interest, and if he has no good quality of life, then it's not *fair* to put him through that."

Mr and Mrs Blakely looked at one another, identical expressions of sorrow etched upon their features, and then down at their struggling, labouring pet.

I bit the inside of my cheek in an attempt to keep my own emotions in some semblance of order. I blinked rapidly to fight back tears. Even though this was not *my* pet, in fact I had never met Buster before this afternoon, it was impossible to not be affected by the retched sadness of the whole situation. I had effectively just informed them that I wanted to kill their dog. But it was my role to consider the impact on the animal, to consider his welfare and what was in his best interest, not just the inevitable grief of the owner. Buster was suffering. If I thought for one moment that medications would solve this problem, or, if not solve it completely, give him some meaningful quality of life for a few more weeks or months, then I would be advising them of that fact. But it wouldn't. Buster was *dying* right here, before their eyes, without any help from me. And it was a horrible, stressful, *painful* death, gasping and struggling for every breath. The least I could do was put an end to that.

"I think -" Mrs Blakely gulped and swallowed a hiccup as she tried to speak. "I don't think we should put him through it. I can't bear to watch him suffer like this any longer. He's been such a good dog, a wonderful companion. I don't want him to suffer at the end."

Her husband nodded his silent agreement as they almost collapsed into one another, dissolving into uncontrollable floods of tears.

For Buster, this was the end of the road.

I felt uncomfortably like a voyeur to their grief, shifting back onto my heels in an attempt to give them some semblance of space. A rapid flurry of eyebrow semaphore communicated with Jess the need for tissues, a euthanasia consent form and my own growing panic at what I was about to undertake.

This was the first 'put to sleep' I had performed completely by myself, without the security blanket of at least another vet in the building. It was my responsibility to ensure Buster's passing was as stress-free and as painless as humanly possible. It was down to me to be able to hit a vein in a dog with severe vascular compromise; a difficult enough proposal for an experienced veterinary surgeon, never mind a newly employed baby vet. I tried to breathe through the adrenaline hit that shook my nerves until I swore my teeth rattled. I swallowed again and again, feeling as though my rapidly pounding heart was lodged in my throat and I couldn't quite take a big enough breath because of it.

"Have you ever had an animal put to sleep before?" I queried several minutes later, once Buster's owners had managed to contain their grief and were capable of conversing coherently, unsurprised by the hitch in my own voice and frantically trying to recall all those communication skills lectures that went into this exact situation with excruciating, mind-numbing detail. All I came up with was a blank; a dark void of impending doom and inadequacy that threatened to undermine whatever confidence I had ever had in my ability to do this.

A strangled "No," was their response.

"What we're going to do is inject Buster with, what is essentially, an overdose of an anaesthetic agent," I continued in what I hoped was a calm, professional tone, but failed miserably. I had observed enough vets do this, I should have been quietly confident, but I was anything but. It was a totally different matter when I was the one who was responsible for the situation, and I was barely able to think or function through the crippling nerves and thundering adrenaline. "Buster is just going to fall asleep, and not wake up. His heart and his lungs will stop. He won't feel any pain, just a sharp prick as the needle goes in, and it might feel a little cold as we proceed with the injection. Sometimes a dog can have a little twitch, sometimes they can gasp a little or make a little noise. That's perfectly normal, and it's not a conscious reaction; just a nervous reaction, the electrical energy left in his muscles dissipating. He won't be in any discomfort or distress, and by the time any of that occurs he will already be gone."

I paused a moment to allow my words to sink in. Glancing between the couple I took a deep breath. So far, I hadn't made any serious errors, but I hadn't got to the most difficult part of the procedure yet.

"You don't have to stay in the room while it happens if you think it will be too unpleasant for you. If you want, you can say goodbye now and leave him with us or come back in once he's gone."

"No," Mrs Blakely shook her head vehemently, her hand clenched tightly in the thick ruff at the back of Buster's neck, her voice thin and shaky. "I want to stay."

"Yes," her husband seconded; his jaw clenched tightly in a manful struggle to contain his emotions. "He's been with us his whole life; it's not right for us to leave him now."

"Alright," I gave them a brief, sympathetic smile tinged with a double shot of panic and raised my eyebrows at Jess who was hovering in the background awaiting my need of her assistance. She quickly stepped around the couple and their beloved pet, crouching down at his side so she could raise a vein for the injection. Jess operated with a respectful efficiency, she had seen this done many times before and her confidence helped to settled some of my nerves, making my hands steady enough to even think about performing an IV injection. "If you just talk to his head so he knows you're there and there's nothing to be worried about. I'm just going to clip a little hair off his leg here..." I wielded a pair of scissors to snip a patch of fur from Buster's foreleg, gently cooing at the old, exhausted dog as he watched me with wary, sad brown eyes... "I know, Sausage, I'm not a very good hairdresser, am I? Now this is going to be a little cold."

I swabbed his leg with a little surgical spirit on a cotton ball to help make his weak vein stand out more clearly. Another deep breath and a quick mental prayer to whatever god looked after young, inexperienced vets.

"Now, Buster, just a sharp little prick," I advanced the needle into his vein, my heart pounding loudly enough I was certain my companions would be able to hear it. Draw back; there should be blood in the hub... where was the blood in the hub? Re-direct, draw back again, this time there was flash-back of blood, and I felt a surge of triumphant adrenaline kicking my heartrate into overdrive. Buster gave a deep, heavy sigh. My voice wobbled slightly as I was hit by the import of the moment, of the impact on the lives of the owners of this much-loved dog. Buster had been a member of their family for thirteen years. He was an important part of their lives; they'd seen him grow from a tiny baby to an adult to a sick old man. And I was precipitating his death. It didn't matter that it was in Buster's best interest. It didn't matter that if we didn't euthanise him he would undoubtedly suffer a long, painful, distressing demise. It was still a huge, immense act. "And a little bit cold. There now, sweetheart, you just go to sleep."

Buster's head grew heavy and his breathing became slower and slower, each breath coming after a longer and longer pause, until they came no more. He gave a long, low sigh, the painful tension in his frame growing limp and lax. Mrs Blakely uttered a huge sob and crouched over the dog, burying her face in the thick fur at the back of his neck, her husband gently rubbing her back in an attempt to console her grief.

With a jerk of my head I usurped Jess' position, lifting my stethoscope from around my neck and taking a long listen to his broad chest. I even held my breath for a long thirty seconds, trying to calm my own bounding heart so I didn't miss even the most miniscule of beats.

There were none.

Buster was gone. I discretely brushed a tear from my cheek, remembering the deep sadness I had felt almost ten years previously when my ancient family moggy had passed away, and more recently the sheer overwhelming grief I had endured at my own father's funeral.

Mr and Mrs Blakely departed some twenty minutes later, filled with profuse gratitude at the caring, considerate way we had managed Buster's passing, leaving Jess and I with his body, and a promise to contact them when his ashes were returned from the pet crematorium. I wanted to ask them what they were thanking us for. I knew we had given him a dignified, pain-free death, but we had still taken him from them. Unfortunately, I also knew that being affected by client's grief was something that would pass with time and experience. Most vets, if they are to survive any length of time in this profession, develop a certain numbness to the emotions displayed by owners grieving for the passing of their adored pets. While sympathising with the distress of losing an animal, if a vet allowed themselves to be affected by every single pet they put to sleep, they would be irretrievably depressed before they had completed a year in practice.

It felt like I'd been kicked in the chest. My emotions tumbled over one another like a flurry of autumn leaves, and I couldn't grab hold of even one of them long enough to figure out what it was I was really feeling. Sadness, relief, triumph, pride. They all rolled around my head in an unending torrent and I knew I wouldn't be able to sort them into any kind of order anytime soon.

I was happy I'd managed to perform the procedure without any major problems, but it was difficult to be pleased with myself when my success meant an animal was dead.

I was utterly shattered. I was so pathetically grateful I had an experienced nurse to help me through the situation. Jess' calm, practical, while sympathetic, manner had helped me keep my grasp on my nerves. Hitting a vein was something I'd done so many times before, but on such a critical moment, with the knowledge my patient would have really poor circulation and thus very difficult veins, my doubts and fears had threatened to swamp me.

"You did good, Kiddo," Jess wrapped an arm around my shoulders once we were alone and gave me a congratulatory squeeze. "Really good. That wasn't an easy put to sleep by any stretch of the imagination and you handled it really well."

Her quiet, encouraging, congratulation was exactly what I needed to hear.

Locking up the practice, so a client didn't inadvertently walk in on us moving the deceased dog, we placed him in a plastic body bag to prevent leakage of any noxious bodily fluids and lifted him into the large freezer hidden out of sight around the corner at the far end of the building. This would keep him in cold storage, ensuring there were no unpleasant smells to disturb the other clients and the staff, until the crematorium would come and collect him during the next working week.

Jess and I parted ways in a subdued manner, hoping we didn't see one another again until normal business hours on Monday morning.

"Try to get a good night sleep," Jess instructed before getting into her car, giving me a second brief hug. "And a good meal down ya. You'll feel better about everything in the morning."

Death, I reflected as I drove home, was an inevitable part of this profession. As many farmers have said to me subsequently; *where there's livestock, there's dead stock*, and that was no different for domesticated pet animals. Their lives were brief in comparison to our own, but I knew owners did not love their pets any less than they did their other family members. I had to take comfort from the fact that I had given Buster, and would continue to give any animal who came to me in need, a dignified, stress-free, painless passing.

Which, in itself, was a blessing.

CHAPTER SIX

May is for Madness

May began with my eldest brother's wedding. He was marrying a very lovely lady, who was incidentally a registered veterinary nurse, and whom I thought ought to be canonised for putting up with him. I love my brother, both of them in fact, but I have found that Matthew and I get on far better now than we ever did growing up, mostly because we are separated by several very large counties. Any longer than a week under the same roof and we start to fall out, and I certainly wouldn't be able to live with him without considering the merits of smothering him with a pillow. Although to be honest, he would probably say the exact same thing about me.

The wedding came off with jubilant chaos as all such events did, and I bridesmaided with great aplomb. I even managed to not fall flat on my face while walking in my floor length dress, not stumble over the words of my reading and remembered to keep my dinner-time conversation to completely non-veterinary topics so as not to gross out my fellow diners. My second brother's best man speech had everyone in stitches, practically rolling in the aisles, and when he gave a description of Matthew's four-point plan for tying his shoelaces I almost died laughing.

On my way back to Durham, in the murky dim of twilight as I was driving past Raby Castle, a deer raced across the road, almost clipping the bonnet of my car as I screeched to a shuddering, heart-pounding stop. My hands were shaking and my eyes felt as though they were popping out of my head with the shock of the near collision. Almost exactly the same way I'd felt the first time I had been presented with a small animal case that wasn't a simple vaccination, flea, worming. Deer were not small creatures, and not only might it have done a serious amount of damage to the vehicle, at national speed-limit it was likely to have injured me as well. I didn't think Andrew would have thanked me for not only writing off the car, but myself, within the first month of my employment.

May started crazy and steadily went downhill from there.

It began with a veritable epidemic of colic.

I don't think a day went by I didn't see a colicky horse, some of them twice in a twenty-four-hour period in order to administer intravenous medication at either end of the day. Although on a plus point it did seriously improve my ability to hit an equine jugular vein with confident accuracy. I even overcame my aversion to Shetland pony necks as I was sent out, under protest, to see several of them during this time.

None of *them* gave me a black eye though, so that might have had something to do with it!

Unfortunately, one or two of my patients didn't improve with medication alone, which is sometimes the case, and their owners couldn't afford referral to a specialist equine practice where surgery would be an option. In that instance the only option we could offer was to relieve any pain or suffering by putting them to sleep.

It was an inevitable part of horse ownership. They were beautiful creatures, but they were in many cases physically delicate. And even if they *did* go to surgery there was no guarantee they would survive the anaesthetic, or the recovery period afterwards.

It was not an experience I would wish on my worst enemy.

The majority of horse euthanasia are straightforward events. A bolus injection of a drug that will stop their hearts, and most of them go very quietly and very peaceful into the long goodnight. On the other hand, those that do not can be incredibly traumatic.

This surfeit of horse calls introduced me not only to a large number of the practice clients, but also to a peculiarity of Co Durham I have not come across anywhere before or since.

Carefully following the directions to yet another poorly horse, I ended up driving into a narrow street of terrace houses, barely wide enough to squeeze my car down, completely certain I had got lost once again. I walked with some trepidation toward number 17, as I had been instructed and knocked on the door, certain that the residents were going to laugh at my mistake. My knock was answered by a tall, older man in grubby jeans and tee shirt with a cigarette hanging half smoked from his mouth. This wasn't exactly the most affluent area of Stanley, and it could be a bit rough, so I was dutifully a little anxious about the whole scenario.

"Hello, I'm Gwen from Oakbank Veterinary Surgery," I started off confidently, determined not to show my trepidation, but tapered off a little as I continued. "I'm here to see a horse?"

I knew I sounded as uncertain as I felt.

He squinted at me for a long moment, obviously judging me by my stature and appearance.

"Horse's through here," he said, opening the door further to gesture me into the dark hallway.

His response didn't do anything for my utter confusion. I followed him into the house, through the kitchen, trying to suspend my disbelief, and ultimately into the back yard of the property, where there was indeed a horse.

My face had to have reflected my astonishment. There was a *horse* in the back yard. Although it was more of a pony really, but still; there was definitely an equine outside the back door.

"How did you get him in here?" I asked, my curiosity piqued by the oddness of the situation.

"Through the front door," the owner answered in a gruff tone that seemed to question why I was asking him to state the obvious.

I wondered how on earth they were going to get him out if he wasn't capable of walking under his own steam.

The yard itself wasn't particularly huge; what had obviously at one point been the coal bunker transformed into a lean-to shelter for the pony in adverse weather and cobbled underfoot. Several large hay-nets festooned the side of the shelter and the fence around the yard. It couldn't have been much more than fifty feet long and maybe thirty feet wide, not what I would consider big enough to provide much comfort or exercise for a horse, but, as I was to learn, it was not an uncommon occurrence in this part of the world.

The pony was a pie-bald trotter-type who was standing in the far corner of the yard, head down and flanks twitching miserably. Smears of dirt almost obscured the white of his coat in several places and his sides were heaving as he struggled to draw breath into his lungs. Several other people populated the yard, a couple of younger men and a few girls, all of whom were idly watching the pony with various degrees of concern.

"So what have we got here?" I began the conversation with false bravado, not wanting to let on that I was quite significantly intimidated by the number of eyes watching me, judging me.

"He's been off his grub for a couple days," one of the younger men piped up. "Not been hisself."

"And he's been thrashing and rolling quite a lot," one of the young girls spoke, her face creased with concern and I could clearly see the tracks of tears on her cheeks. "This is the first he's stood still for the last half hour."

I approached the depressed pony and began a clinical exam, which by this point, after so many colics in such quick succession; I could probably do in my sleep. His heartrate was elevated... very elevated, his gut sounds depressed. I began to get a very nervous, very unhappy feeling in my stomach. Crouching down I checked the pulses in his heels and the under the curve of his jaw, feeling them bounding at a rapid pace beneath my fingertips. A look in his mouth revealed gums that should have been a nice pale pink were a bright, angry red with livid purple rings circling his teeth.

My heart sank, settling like a lump of lead in my stomach making me feel nauseous.

I wanted to close my eyes and pretend this wasn't happening to me. I wanted to rewind the morning and make Andrew or Carl go on this call instead of me.

Those purple rings on vivid red gums meant that this pony was toxic. Without having the ability to look inside his belly and see exactly what was going on I couldn't diagnose the reason why, but it was likely catastrophic. A piece of his gut had probably got trapped somewhere and there was now bacteria in his blood, causing not only his intestine, but his other organs to not function properly.

He needed serious intervention immediately. My brain instantly began to scroll through the list of what he would require; IV antibiotic, intravenous fluids, pain relief, an ultrasound at least, likely abdominal surgery to correct what it was that had gone wrong. And there was absolutely no guarantee he would even survive the journey to the referral centre.

It was going to cost thousands and thousands of pounds, and I was doubtful his owners could, or would, pay that amount of money in the attempt to save him.

Just as I was about to open my mouth and try to break the news, gently, somehow, the pony jerked and dropped to the ground. A warning was shouted and with the quick instincts of self-preservation everyone in the yard dived out of the way. Heart pounding in my ears I watched the poor animal thrash and roll on his side, throwing his head and whinnying in distress and abject misery.

The older man who had met me at the door turned to me with his face pale and sadness in his eyes.

"Just put him down," he gruffly growled out the words. "He's had it, like."

I couldn't help but agree with him.

"Do you have anywhere that it would be easier to move him after he's gone?" I asked in a low voice after I had gone back to my car to get sedation and Somulose to euthanise the horse.

The young girls were weeping piteously, and I didn't want them to overhear the conversation. It already didn't help that I was almost shaking with nerves.

"There's a green out back, pet," he suggested, roughly gesturing toward the back alley at the end of the yard. "Might get him out that way, if he'll walk."

In one of his reasonably still moments I managed to place an IV catheter in his jugular, despite the stress and risk of injury in this situation I wanted to give a mental fist-pump that I had succeeded first time. I knew I wasn't going to get too many chances to make mistakes in the next few minutes, and I could almost feel my throat thickening with anxiety.

This potentially dangerous situation was my responsibility. A horse thrashing and rolling like this in such a confined space was no laughing matter. If any of these people got hurt, despite it being *their* animal, because I was the attending professional, it would be *my* fault. I would be liable.

It wasn't the sort of thought that made my nerves any steadier.

A bolus of sedation helped to give the pony some relief. Within moments he stood swaying woozily on his feet, nose practically scraping the cobbles. I'd given him a little more than the standard dose in my frantic need to stop him from throwing himself around and I immediately began to second-guess the wisdom of my decision. What if it meant he couldn't walk? What if he fell on one of the people around him?

My voice was higher and thinner than usual as I organised the people around me into coaxing the sleepy pony into moving out of the yard, thankful we weren't trying to take him *through the house*! Step after slow step we managed to encourage him out of the door onto the back alley. It was a tight squeeze, and for a moment I thought we might not manage it, instinctively sucking in my own stomach as he scraped his flanks on either side of the gatepost. It appeared he had lost weight in the last couple of days, which was the only reason we didn't have to scrap this plan and consider taking him out the way he'd come in!

I was sweating profusely by the time we finally made it to the small patch of waste-ground between the terrace houses that had been advertised as 'the green'. It was a struggle to draw up the correct amount of the drug I needed. It was so thick and viscous my wrists and fingers whined in protest as I tried to get it into the largest syringe I could find in my car, but eventually I managed it. Warning everyone but the person holding the pony's lead-rein to stand well back I uncapped my catheter and injected.

The pony dropped.

And rolled. And rolled. And rolled.

The girls behind me screamed in distress and I had to shout at the lad holding the bridle to let go as the horse thrashed again. We both had to scarper quick-sharp as long equine limbs spasmed dangerously close to where we were standing.

And there wasn't a single thing I could do to stop it.

It seemed to last for an eternity; a brutal, horrendous lifetime of rolling, thrashing, waving legs and head and neck. Of destroyed plants and flattened, churned up grass, while my heart hammered in my mouth and I had to fight the desire to break down into tears. But it couldn't have been longer than a couple of minutes at the most.

Finally, when everything was still and silent, I made my careful way over to the pony and listened to his soundless chest, checking all his reflexes were gone.

He was dead.

I couldn't look at the crying, wailing girls in the eye as I spoke parting words to the older gentleman and dragged my weary, exhausted body back to the car. Parking several streets away I covered my face with my hands and cried until my throat hurt and my eyes felt as though I'd scrubbed at them with wire-wool.

Eventually I managed to pull myself together enough to make my way back to the practice, hoping that no one would ask me what was wrong. I snuck stealthily in through the back door, immediately seeing the beautiful bouquet, card and box of chocolates on the prep-room table. Picking up the card I saw it was from the Blakelys. They hadn't been able to face coming into the practice immediately after losing Buster, but they really wanted us to know how grateful they were for what we had done for them.

We always seemed to get more cards and chocolate, more genuine gratitude from people whose animals we had put to sleep than from those we managed to fix.

That day it was too much.

I sat down on the step in the kennel room and cried into my hands as though the world was ending.

Moments later I felt the warmth of people seating themselves on either side of me and a mug of strong hot tea was thrust into my hands. I peeked over the rim to see the rest of the staff, aside from Andrew who was busy on his own calls, looking at me with concern. Jess and Leah each squeezed a shoulder in silent support and solidarity. Gwen pried the lid off the chocolates and held it out toward me with a sad, understanding expression on her face.

"Chocolate?"

The offer made me laugh, when I thought I'd never laugh again, and I picked out a rich looking truffle. It helped to remind me that just because the morning had not gone well, it wasn't the end of the world.

I would have good days, and I would have bad days, but with an understanding and supportive team around me, I knew I'd be alright.

CHAPTER SEVEN

May... The madness continues

About a week later I entered the practice in the morning to be greeted by both Andrew and Carl looking a little guilty. I narrowed my eyes at the two men, wondering what on earth they were up to now.

"Pico Dalfour is here for his nail-clip," Andrew dead-panned, but his eyes were bright with wicked delight. "It's for you."

Leah and Jess sniggered behind him, and I suspected I was missing out on something important. I suspected I was being set up for something less than pleasant.

"Take one for the team, Gwen," Carl patted my shoulder. "I'd do it, but last time he almost chewed off my thumb, and I need all my fingers for surgery this morning. See?"

He very thoughtfully showed me the aforementioned digit, complete with a near perfect scarred impression of teeth almost totally encircling the base. I felt the bottom drop out of my stomach. Although it sounded like a simple enough task, nail-clipping could be an utter nightmare in the wrong circumstances; such as an aggressive dog, or black nails, or even one that just wouldn't sit still.

"Plus, neither of us want to be sued for sexual harassment," Andrew added somewhat cryptically that had my eyebrows shooting up to join my hairline.

This was getting weirder and weirder the longer the conversation continued.

"Err okay," I said hesitantly, more than a little uneasy about what I was letting myself in for. "But one of *you* is going to have to hold it ..." I pointed at Leah and Jess, seeing Leah quickly disappear into the back of the practice, leaving her co-conspirator to face the music. My grin might have been slightly evil ... "And it looks like it's going to be you!"

"Great!" Jess said with a roll of her eyes and a resigned expression.

I called the dreaded creature into my consult room, mildly surprised to see that Pico was in fact a Chihuahua, and not the massive, uncontrollable beast I had been envisioning. In my head the dog had been a towering, seven-foot colossus of muscle and teeth, not an animal small enough to fit into my shoe. Although, upon reflection, this was probably worse than if it had been some sort of hound from hell. At least with a big dog you can get a good grip on them without fearing you're going to snap them in half or suffocate them.

Pico's owner, Ms Dalfour, was a woman in her forties with an abundance of figure and a tiny tank-top that was insufficient to adequately contain it. Her bra was quite easily visible above the neckline of her top, and Pico the Chihuahua was happily nestled between her sizeable breasts.

I think I understood what Andrew had been driving at now.

Pico was what I had begun to call a 'boob-dog'. That is to say a small designer dog that probably never walked anywhere in its life but spent almost his entire life clutched to his owner's chest. Sometimes it was difficult to get owners of these particular dogs to put them down on the examination table during a consultation, and due to this I have subsequently inadvertently groped several women while attempting to perform a clinical exam, and once almost vaccinated some woman's boob because the tiny dog jumped and the needle went all the way through.

It was utterly ridiculous and made the life of the vet and veterinary nurse so much more difficult than if they would just relinquish their beloved pet for five minutes.

Armed with a tiny muzzle that would have been cute if not for the reason it was required, I began my campaign to liberate Pico from Ms Dalfour's chest. Surely it would be safer, and far less embarrassing for everyone involved.

"If you could just pop him on the table for me," I began in an assertive tone, hoping I sounded efficient and no-nonsense so that she would obey me without question. Sometimes it was all in the turn of phrase and tone of voice. "We'll just put a little muzzle on him and get those nails trimmed."

Unfortunately, Ms Dalfour proved irritatingly resistant to commanding compulsion. I shouldn't have been surprised.

I ignored Jess' slight smirk at my ultimately unsuccessful attempt.

"Oh no!" Ms Dalfour trilled in an overblown, theatrical voice, my suggestion only causing her to clutch the tiny dog even closer to her overflowing bosom. "No! My poor little darling doesn't need a muzzle, do you baby, no you don't. Don't let the mean vet lady upset you, my precious."

I suddenly got a mental image of a hunched, hairless version of the nightmare client in front of me bent over a golden ring, hissing imprecations against 'nasty hobbitses' and had to bite my tongue to stop myself from giggling somewhat hysterically. Sometimes the places my brain wandered to were just not appropriate for the sensible, responsible professional I was trying to pretend to be.

She continued to make smoochy, baby noises at the dog and I was forced to keep my expression neutral when all I wanted to do was gag. I heard Jess make an odd snorting sound that was undoubtedly a stifled laugh. I began to think of way I could get even with my bosses later for inflicting this woman on me.

This was definitely going to be more difficult than I thought.

"Well then, I'll just get Jess to hold onto him for me, so he doesn't bear any grudges toward you," it was said in a hopeful manner, perhaps implying the dog might dislike her because of the imminent procedure would be enough to persuade Ms Dalfour to acquiesce to my less than subtle hint.

My suggestion was met with another negative and I just about restrained a sigh of annoyance. The dog's claws needed clipping and I was trying to help the woman, could she just not cooperate?

Eventually, when I was actually considering just wrestling the dog from her grasp and being done with it, Pico was deposited upon the table-top with a huff and a turned-up nose. Jess quickly moved to grip the recalcitrant Chihuahua in a headlock. Before she'd even touched him, he started to squeal and snarl and generally turn into the Tasmanian Devil on speed. His little mouth opened wide as he thrashed his head violently trying to snag any appendage within chewing distance to sink his teeth into. His already bug eyes bulged even further, and I admitted a private worry that they would pop out altogether if we weren't careful.

I hadn't even done anything to him yet!

Ms Dalfour flittered about to the side of us, uttering high-pitched noises of distress.

"Oh! You're hurting him. Oh my poor baby! Don't hurt him!"

I grimly ignored her ridiculousness, inwardly grousing that we wouldn't be in this situation if she either allowed the dog to *walk*, or if she had socialised it better when it was a puppy, and trying valiantly to also disregard the way the tiny dog's hind claws were currently removing layers of skin from my forearm.

"We're not hurting him, Ms Dalfour," Jess chimed in reassuringly as she maintained her white-knuckled grip on the miniature demon we were grappling with, evidently seeing I was too busy trying to clip nails without removing the entire toe to answer. "He's just being soft."

Several rapid snips later and we were finished. A greatly relieved breath exploded from my lungs.

"Done!" I announced, perhaps louder than strictly necessary, and Jess gratefully released Pico from her hold and took a long step away from the consulting table in the event the tiny monster tried to take his ire out on one or both of us.

Ms Dalfour swooped down on her pet, scooping the Chihuahua back into her voluminous, smothering embrace and clutching him tightly to her.

"Poor Pico," she cooed at the panting, shaking, snarling animal. "What did the nasty lady do to you? Poor, little lamb. Mummy has you now, you're safe."

"You're welcome, Ms Dalfour," I returned, trying to keep the sarcasm out of my tone, covertly examining the red, angry lines from Chihuahua claws that were glaringly evident on my abused skin.

She merely sniffed at me in acknowledgement and set sail like a galleon at sea back out into the waiting room. I raised my eyebrows at Jess in astonishment. Not even a thank you seemed to be forthcoming despite how evidently difficult it had been to perform the task *she* had requested of us. I didn't expect everyone to be overflowing with gratitude for every little service, but it would at least have been nice to have some concession due to the amount of trouble and effort her pet had put us through.

Some people were just rude.

"Is she for real?" I asked in a whisper, since it was never good practice to talk about a client while they were still in the waiting room, but I just couldn't keep the words trapped behind my lips any longer.

"Yup," Jess' answer came with a resigned shrug and a rueful twist of her mouth. "At least we've both got all our fingers and you didn't make him bleed."

I could only shake my head in disbelief. Nothing certain members of the public did could ever surprise me anymore.

CHAPTER EIGHT

I no longer like May

After that, May became the month of difficult pregnancies.
At six o'clock on a Friday night, on a weekend I wasn't on call, one of the farms rang in to request assistance to calve a cow. Unfortunately, Andrew whose weekend it actually was, had already gone out to replace a cow's prolapsed uterus, leaving me to hold the fort, as it was Carl's half day off.

So, after I had wrapped up the remainder of evening surgery, I trundled up to Hogshead Farm, which was also a boarding house and cycling café as it was on the coast-to-coast cycle route, to investigate what the problem seemed to be. I was internally hoping it was something relatively simple as I was supposed to be driving back home to my mother's house this weekend, and I didn't much fancy a two-hour journey after a long and arduous battle to get a calf out.

As always, the Gods of Veterinary Medicine weren't smiling upon me.

When I arrived, I discovered the cow in question was but fifteen months old – the age most heifers are just about to go to the bull or be served by artificial insemination – and struggling to birth what I considered a complete monster of a calf. She was down on her side in a pen, looking completely and utterly dejected. It turned out that the heifer had been caught accidentally when a bull had jumped the fence, and although the owner – incidentally she wasn't owned by our clients, they were just boarding a number of his stock for him – knew she'd been mated, he hadn't thought to do anything about it.

I fought the desire to roll my eyes and chomped back the irritated words dancing on the tip of my tongue. All it would have taken was a single injection to ensure this didn't happen, but now we were in this situation with a cow that would probably be fit for nothing but the slaughterhouse after such an ordeal, if she survived at all.

"It's a bloody shame," Mr Dawson shook his head sadly as he walked me over to the pen, carrying several items of my equipment. I had been up here once or twice before for lambings, and I rather liked the family. They were all very polite and quite willing to lend a hand if the circumstances required it. "We didn't even realise she was in calf until I came back to check them this evening and found her straining."

"We'll see what we can do," I returned, getting down on my knees and quickly surveying what had occurred before my arrival. "But it might be an out-the-side-door job since she's so small. Have you had a pull at her at all?"

"We didn't think it was a good idea," he said quickly. "It looks pretty tightly wedged."

The Red Poll heifer had managed to pass the head of the calf through her pelvis, and that was where it had stuck. The calf was quite obviously dead, the foetal fluids drying on its coat and its blue distended tongue protruding at a gross angle from its mouth. Lathering a generous amount of lube onto my hand and forearm I did what I could to work my hand around the massive head to enter the cervix and determine how much room, if any, I had to work with. And that was where I hit my first impediment. As small as my hands were, I couldn't get them into her. The head was in the way and there was no room to push it back inside.

I uttered a heavy sigh. The head was going to have to come off.

Embryotomy – the removal of a foetus in several pieces when the animal is dead and too large to naturally pass through the pelvic canal

– is not, in theory, a difficult practice. The foetus is sectioned into segments, generally, if the calf is coming headfirst, split perpendicular to the spine at the level of the last rib, and then the spine itself split roughly down the middle to halve the width of the calf and ease delivery. Which is much easier said than done and far simpler in a classroom, demonstration environment, than on your hands and knees in a dimly lit calving pen.

Of course, it would also have been much easier if I'd had more of the calf to work with.

Several cuts with a scalpel blade later and I had managed to disarticulate the head, placing it gently in a corner. To one side I saw one of the farmhands quickly vacate the pen, his face a little green and pale, his stomach evidently turned by the decapitation. Placing my open hand against the stump of the neck I tried to push the rest of the calf back through the pelvic canal so I could get access to the rest of the body. It wouldn't be a simple task to section it into pieces completely inside the uterus and might even cause further damage to the mother by the use of embryotomy wire, which resembles heavy-duty cheese-wire.

Even with half a bottle of lube squirted around the edges of the stump and some considerable force it just wasn't going to budge. The mother grunted and strained against me, her flanks rising and falling in a rapid rhythm, her blood-shot eyes rolling all the way back into her skull so only the whites were visible.

I wasn't getting anywhere, and the cow was starting to become distressed. A glance at my watch revealed to my astonishment that I had been here for just under an hour. Time always seemed to speed up when grappling around on the floor with a calf that just didn't want to come.

Sitting back on my knees I stripped off my parlour-top to remove the practice tee-shirt I was wearing underneath, leaving me in a sweat-soaked vest-top and waterproof leggings. It was a very warm May evening and the pen was incredibly stuffy. My mouth was parched, and I felt as though I was becoming dehydrated as well as out of breath and as red as a tomato in the face.

"It's not going to move," I uttered the verdict with an irritated huff, swiping hair off my forehead with the back of my forearm and instantly regretting it as I managed to smear lube and foetal fluids onto my skin. Although I can honestly say, years later, that's not the worst thing I've ever had on my face. "We've got two options; we open her up and get the calf out that way, or we put her to sleep."

A brutal frown furrowed Mr Dawson's brow as he looked from me to the panting, moaning creature at my side. Honestly, she wasn't in a good way. I wasn't certain she would be able to cope with a caesarean, but cows are marvellous animals. They can fall over on their internal organs, roll them into the mud and muck, and still survive relatively problem free. And then sometimes they just die for no apparent reason.

"I'm not sure he'll want to spend the money on a caesar, not the way she is now," Mr Dawson replied in annoyance. "He should have spent a couple a quid when he realised the bull had jumped the fence and we wouldn't all be here now!"

His words exactly mirrored my earlier thoughts and I was glad I wasn't the only one thinking it. I huffed another irritated sigh and heaved myself to my feet.

"Well, let's see if she'll make the decision for us," I suggested more calmly than I actually felt. I was annoyed. This was a waste of a life if we ended up having to euthanise her and would undoubtedly affect her fertility for the remainder of her existence. And it wasn't necessary. In fact, it was easily fixable. I uttered a few choice words under my breath quiet enough so no one would overhear. "If she can get up there's a chance of saving her, if not I suppose that's that then."

Mr Dawson moved over to the cow and gave her a slap upon the rump, digging his boot not unkindly into her belly in an attempt to prompt her to get to her feet. It had the opposite effect. Instead of even struggling to stand the cow threw its head back, arching its neck, her whole body shuddering and shaking. It wasn't a contraction or straining to pass the calf. I don't quite know *what* it was. Although I had a feeling it was an answer to the question regardless.

I pinched the sensitive skin between her cleats, hoping to provoke a reaction, hoping she would acknowledge the pain and withdraw her foot. Nothing happened. I tried again on her other hind claw and received the same response. Nothing.

Trying to pass her monstrous calf had likely crushed the nerves around the rim of the pelvis, leading to a paralysis of the hind limbs. It was another strike against her.

"I don't think she's getting up," Mr Dawson said unhappily.

"No," I agreed. "Which gives us our answer, I suppose."

Mr Dawson rang the owner, who agreed with our assessment of the situation and readily gave his permission to put the cow to sleep.

I returned to my car and dug out a bottle of Somulose. Oakbank didn't have a captive bolt gun for the humane slaughter of cattle, so we had to inject into the vein if we wanted to euthanise an animal. I drew up 50ml of the thick, gloopy fluid, inwardly raging at how easy this would have been to prevent, and quickly injected the whole syringe into the jugular vein. Within moments she was dead.

Euthanising a farm animal wasn't the same as performing the same task on a pet. It's not that there is no emotion involved in the procedure, but farmers are surrounded by life and death on seemingly a daily basis, the same as most vets, and they became almost immune to the practice. But this time I was angry at how unfair the whole situation was. Nobody wanted to see an animal go in this manner. This needn't have happened if the farmer was more careful with his stock. I quickly cleaned up my kit and myself and headed home in a fine mood, stopping for pizza on the way, because nothing was better after a bad day at work than hot, melted, gooey cheese.

Stress eating wasn't good for my waistline or my health, but it was something I found myself doing with worrying frequency after seeing certain clients or going on some visits. My only consolation was it was only pizza and chips and not alcohol.

Thankfully my next difficult birth ended in a much happier manner.

Toward the end of May I was called out to the small holding of a pleasant, but incredibly eccentric couple; Mr and Mrs Gill of Brookbank Place. He had made rather a lot of money in the City during his younger years, but after a stress-induced heart attack in his late thirties the pair had packed up and moved to more Northern climes in search of essentially *The Good Life*. They had a number of rare breed cattle, a small flock of sheep, several goats and an assorted collection of different kinds of fowl.

Their farm consisted of several sheds in which various animals were housed, a couple of large poly-tunnels forming a small nursery of plants and a static caravan which contained the produce of their animals for sale.

My patient for that day was a Mule ewe affectionately known as 'Specks', because of her speckled head. She had quite unhelpfully prolapsed her vagina in the process of lambing, which needed returning to its proper place before we made the decision of how to get the lambs out.

Mr Gill chased the ewe around the shed for several minutes, the mass of flesh hanging from her backend, flapping and slapping out behind her in a manner that made me wince. It boggled the mind just exactly how she managed to stand, never mind elude capture like that.

Eventually the ewe was cornered and brought to the ground on her back with her back legs held in a tight grip so she couldn't kick me in the face.

"We've got you now, Specks," Mr Gill spoke fondly to the upside-down sheep as she bleated at the indignity of her current position. "Now be a good girl and let Gwen get you sorted. We've got lambs to come out yet."

I couldn't help but smile at his attitude toward his stock. In truth they were all more like pets, or long-term family friends, than livestock, and I liked that about him and his wife.

"Alright then, Sheep-y," I said after numbing the area with an epidural and had arranged my equipment to my liking; clean plastic sheet between the ground and the inverted organ, a bucket of warm water – luxury! – at my side with a bottle of hibiscrub ready to squirt onto the straw-smeared mass of flesh. "Let's have at it, no pushing please!"

Picking off as much of the detritus of the shed as I could, I gave the uterus a thorough clean and a good coating of lubrication to ease its passage back inside the sheep. Unfortunately, that was where the simplicity ended.

Due to a compromised blood supply the uterus had swelled and was now bigger than the hole it had come out of, making replacing the prolapse more difficult than it otherwise would have been, not that it was an easy task in the first place! Generally, I'd get the whole mass back in save for the last few inches, and the animal would give a great heave and shove the entire lot back out at me.

Careful not to put my fingers through the fragile tissue or tear off any of the protruding caruncles, with gentle persistence and patience I managed to persuade the uterus back to where it belonged. And it only took half an hour! However, even though I could get my hand and forearm into the pelvic canal, although it was a little bit of a tight squeeze, there was no way the lamb I encountered was going to come out the same way. Its head and feet were too big for me to even consider giving it a pull, which led me to the conclusion that I would have to perform my first caesarean section; on my own, with no help or guidance from a more experienced vet.

Gulp.

I knew the principle of the surgery and had seen it done enough times that I knew what *should* happen but knowing and doing were two entirely different things. As I returned to my car to collect my equipment, I took several deep, calming breaths, trying to settle the storming cascade of manic butterflies currently staging a revolt in my stomach. Lugging the caesar kit into the shed I desperately tried to compile a mental list of everything I would need before I started; clippers, local anaesthetic, surgical instruments, suture material, something to flush the abdomen with should it become contaminated with foetal fluids… had I missed something? I was certain that there was something not on my list that was crucial to the operation.

I surveyed the items laid out on my make-shift table – a small hay bale – and felt like smacking myself in the forehead. A scalpel blade would be rather useful now, wouldn't it?

My hands shook with nervous tension and my breathing was quicker than I would have liked as I clipped the fleece in a neat square off the left flank, probably a much larger area than I actually needed, but there was no time to worry about that now. Mr Gill smiled at me with kind eyes as I poured neat iodine onto the shaved area and proceeded to perform a farm-animal version of a surgical scrub. He could probably see my trepidation.

"I hope you don't have to be somewhere anytime soon," I made a weak joke in an attempt to keep my mind off the seriousness of what I was about to do.

Adrenaline crawled over my skin like tiny little spiders and I had to fight the urge to scratch at them. My scalp tingled as though someone had just tipped a bucket of tepid water over my head, and I really wished that Andrew or Carl, or even one of the nurses, could have been there with me, just to reassure me that I was doing the right thing in the right order.

"I've got all the time in the world," Mr Gill assured me in a calm tone. "Just take your time."

It was exactly the right thing for him to say and helped to ease some of the jitters that skittered down my spine. Beneath my trusty parlour top my tee shirt was drenched with anxious sweat.

I was suddenly, immensely glad that *this* was the first caesar I was performing, that I wasn't doing it on one of the more commercial farms with more judgemental, critical farmers looking on with suspicious eyes. Mr Gill was an amateur farmer, and sometimes I felt like I was an amateur vet playing at being a professional.

I applied a local anaesthetic block to the left flank just behind the last rib and gave it several minutes to start working before I even thought about putting a scalpel anywhere near the sheep. I probably used far too much, meaning that the practice made no profit on the procedure, but without anyone to tell me the ideal dose I decided I couldn't be too careful. After all I really didn't want Specks to feel what I was about to do. I knew I wouldn't want to.

Gripping the scalpel blade tightly between shaking fingers I mentally gave myself a slap, told myself to be brave and made my first incision.

I wasn't using a scalpel blade handle because of a horror story Andrew had so helpfully told me several weeks previously. Apparently his first boss had always used a handle, but when he was castrating calves one day, one of the calves had kicked the scalpel out of his hand and due to the added weight and momentum of the handle it had ended up landing buried in his thigh.

I wasn't keen on that happening to me.

Skin parted beneath my blade to reveal the bright white of fat and then the thick, juicy red of muscle. The iron tang of blood perfumed the air as it oozed from the edges of my incision and I swallowed down the uncertainty of whether I was doing it right. So far it looked like every other caesar I'd ever seen. I needed to stop second guessing myself, but it was so difficult when doing something new and knowing that I was supposed to know what I was up to and the potential difficulties that could arise. Not only that I was supposed to know how to fix them, when I didn't think that shouting for help, and maybe crying, was the right answer.

Thankfully, the operation progressed without any major technical hitches, and just over an hour later two live lambs were shaking gunk and straw out of their ears and bleating while I placed the last skin suture into the baa-ing mother. Once she was released, she immediately hopped to her feet and staggered over to the lambs, frantically licking and nuzzling at her babies. Specks, it seemed, was going to be a good mother.

With much less speed, I scraped myself off the floor and cleaned myself up before packing my used kit back into the rest of the box to be re-sterilised at the practice. My back felt as though it had a permanent kink in it and my knees weren't happy with me either from that length of time kneeling on the floor, but I gritted my teeth against the pain and hauled my stuff back to the car.

Mr Gill disappeared momentarily as I was scrubbing at my waterproofs to get them as clean as possible, returning moments later with a packet of bacon and sausages from their butcher's shop. His grin lit up his jovial features as he saw the desperate avarice that I knew flooded my features. I'm a strange creature, but nothing spoke to my heart quite like bacon, and I could envision a good fry-up for tea with those tasty looking morsels.

"You deserve it," he said as he handed me the paper-wrapped package. "You did a really good job today."

"Thank you," I returned quietly, fighting the sudden prickle of tears that I had to rapidly blink back before I made an utter fool of myself at his praise and gratitude. "That's really kind of you."

"Nothing to it," he shrugged off my words. "You made sure that Specks was going to be ok."

When I finally pulled out of the farmyard, I had to force myself to concentrate on the road as I came down from the adrenaline high of performing a caesar all on my own for the first time. I felt sick and hungry and tired and elated all at the same time. I wanted to shout and fist-pump in triumph and put my head on the steering wheel and cry until I couldn't see straight.

Being a veterinary surgeon was an utter rollercoaster of emotion that I hadn't envisioned. But I was rapidly realising that I wouldn't want to do anything else.

CHAPTER NINE

June is for... Pardon me, what did you just say?

The on-call phone rang at ten o'clock on a Friday night, as I was lying semi-conscious on the sofa watching TV. I almost fell off the sofa as I grabbed for the little black harbinger of doom – to this day the Nokia theme gives me cold shivers – and probably sounded more than a little breathless as I answered with;

"Oakbank Vets, emergency, how can I help?" I thought it sounded like a confident and professional way to answer an emergency phone line – stress the *emergency*.

"Who's that?" a thinnish masculine voice asked on the other end. I didn't recognise the voice.

"It's Gwen," I returned patiently. "What can I do for you?"

"I haven't met you afore," he continued, and I thought he sounded relatively elderly.

"No," I gritted my teeth and tried to remain calm and professional, repeating for the third time, "How can I help?"

"Got a cow calving," was the abrupt response. "It's not comin'. Lightfoot at the Cross House."

I winced in delight. Unfortunately, I had no more idea where he was than before he'd told me his name and address.

"I'm afraid I don't know where you are, would you be able to give me some directions?"

I took down his instructions, without much hope of being able to find him as they were quite confused and hauled myself off the sofa and into the car. Once I reached Tow Law and took the turn he'd described I proceeded to drive up and down the same road for a further fifteen minutes getting more and more frustrated as more time passed, before I managed to drive into the correct yard, more by luck than judgement.

Mr Lightfoot was waiting for me beneath the dim illumination of a struggling spotlight and my heart sank just that little bit further at the sight of him. I parked beside the shed he indicated and mentally girded my loins for the ordeal to come.

Calving cows was no easy task, and usually if there was some form of problem it was useful to have at least one other reasonably strong person to lend a hand aside from myself. Mr Lightfoot was a stooped, bent man, not too many inches taller than me, who must have been in his eighth – if not ninth – decade. As he tottered around to the passenger-side door, Mr Lightfoot looked rather frail, as though a strong wind would knock him over completely, and I doubted he would be much use should we need to give it a bit of a tug.

On the other hand, perhaps his idea of 'not coming' and my idea of the same problem were complete opposites. I was hoping that this would be a case of a bit of rearrangement of limbs and head and the calf would happily greet the world without too much trouble.

I could but hope.

Opening my door, I swung one foot out of the car and stepped in slurry up to my ankle. I paused, closed my eyes and fought the urge to face-palm.

Slipping and slithering down the relatively steep slope I was parked on, I wrenched my way into a clean pair of waterproofs and parlour top and collected what I thought I might need. Mr Lightfoot smiled pleasantly at me.

"She's back this way, I've got 'er in the crush already for ya."

Well, at least that was something. The cow in question was a reasonably sized Limousin, a breed not exactly known for their shy and retiring personalities. I'd had a lecturer at university who believed that all Limousin cattle were extremely dangerous and therefore lead deficient.

After scrounging around for something to stand on, the best we could find was a rickety old milk crate that I crossed my fingers and hoped would hold my weight; I lathered up my arm and dove in for a good feel at what was going on. Almost immediately I was greeted by a pair of significantly sized feet. From their shape and orientation, I could immediately tell they were hind-feet, a suspicion confirmed by the rapid discovery of a tail and hind-quarters.

The calf was breach.

Not a particularly good sign.

Neither was the fact the feet crossed the moment they were coaxed into the pelvic canal, or the approximate dimensions of the rear end of the calf.

She wasn't a small cow, but her calf was looking like it was a bit too big to be delivered by natural methods. I felt my mouth instantly become as dry as the Sahara Desert and my heart slam hard enough against my sternum I thought it might bruise.

It was going to have to be a caesarean. If we even attempted to jack out that calf, we'd likely kill it, and perhaps the cow, in the process.

I'd seen plenty of caesars performed, I'd performed the same on sheep without any problems, but there was no way I was going to be flying solo for my first attempt to operate on a cow. Not to mention I'd need some help to actually get the calf out once the incision was made.

"We're going to have to operate," I told Mr Lightfoot as I stepped down from the milk crate, wiping goo from my arm. "Do you have somewhere we can put her and have access to her left side?"

I had noticed the breeze-block walls of the crush with a deep sense of disappointment.

Mr Lightfoot scratched his head for a moment before offering;

"Err, we could tie 'er up in the byer over there," he gestured to the far edge of the feed rail that was next to the concrete wall. "She's a quiet ol' lass, should stand fer ya."

I kept my doubts to myself about the placidity of her temperament and nodded my agreement. There seemed to be no other option.

"Is there anyone that could come and give us a hand?" I asked without much hope of receiving a positive response.

"Nah," he scratched his head again. "Jest me an' the missus."

I inhaled and swallowed the sigh I really wanted to let loose. The last thing I wanted to be doing was my first cow caesarean without sufficient hands to make it light work.

"Right," I tried to smile, but it came out rather thin and nervous. "I'll go grab some stuff and see if I can get some help; I'm rather new at this sort of thing. Could you see if you can get her tied up?"

Without waiting for his reply, I dove back outside to my car and frantically searched for the on-call phone in my trouser pockets. I knew Andrew was away this evening, so I couldn't call him for help, and I hoped Carl was near his phone, or had signal, or hadn't had a drink. Carl wasn't the biggest fan of large animal work, he only really did it when he couldn't otherwise avoid it, but I thought this was something of a special case.

The call connected and rang for several excruciatingly long seconds before going to voicemail. I just about swallowed a hysterical sob.

"Hi, Carl, I've got a cow caesar at Mr Lightfoot's, could you please give me a call back, I could do with a hand," I managed to sound reasonably calm and collected, rather than just simply shouting *help!*

Hanging up I went about gathering my equipment. Thankfully the majority of what I would need was already contained within the black box we fondly called *the caesar kit* meaning I didn't need to think too hard about it. Hefting it off the back-passenger seat I slipped and slid my way back into the shed. The milk-crate was drafted in as my 'table' and I began to lay out my supplies, my thoughts racing a million miles an hour and desperately hoping that Carl would ring me back before I had to get down to the technical nitty-gritty.

In essence it was exactly the same as a sheep caesar… only about twenty times bigger.

Kit, scalpel… don't forget the scalpel this time, Gwen!… local anaesthetic, surgical scrub, needles, syringes… I'm forgetting something! What am I forgetting?

My eye fell on the reels of suture material and I wanted to slap myself on the head. Of course, it would be useful to have something to stitch up the gaping hole I was about to cut in the side of this cow!

I was starting to draw up a few syringes of local anaesthetic to start my block when the on-call phone rang, making me jump out of my skin like a scalded cat. Swiping it off my make-shift table I offered up a prayer to the difficult-to-appease gods of on call that it wasn't *another* call I would have to go to after this one.

Carl's name on the screen made my heart squeeze out several rapid beats of relief.

"What's up, Gwen?" Carl's always calm, laconic voice said soothingly in my ear.

"I've got a cow caesar at The Cross House, and it's just me and Mr Lightfoot," I hoped I didn't sound as agitated as I felt, as though everything in the world except me was in slow-motion. "Could I please get a hand? I've never done one before, and I think I'll need someone to help me get it out."

"Alright," he said without hesitation, and I breathed a sigh of relief. I didn't know why I had been so worried in the first place. My bosses were supportive and wouldn't hang me out to dry. "You get started and I'll be there asap."

The promise of imminent back-up immediately helped to reinstate my confidence in my ability to do what was required of me.

I approached the cow with my shoulders squared and efficiently wielded the clippers to provide a hairless surgical field. I injected the local anaesthetic in an inverted 'L' block to numb the nerves to her skin and muscles on the left flank. While I was waiting for the block to work its magic I poured iodine onto her bare skin, mixing it with a little of the warm water Mr Lightfoot had kindly fetched for me, and giving her a good scrubbing in an attempt to make the procedure as aseptic as possible. It was never going to be a sterile surgical environment, what with the straw and muck and general *cow* of the surroundings, but I wanted to make it as close to ideal as possible.

After ten minutes I did a thorough surgical scrub of my hands and arms and grasped the scalpel blade, giving my incision site an experimental prod with the blade. Since the cow didn't flinch or otherwise try to kick me – although she did have her head in the trough scoffing silage and cake – I decided my anaesthesia was successful and, taking a deep breath, giving myself a mental pep-talk, I made my incision.

Tough, leather-like hide parted beneath the sharp edge of my blade with almost too much ease. The inch of fat underneath peeled back and almost before I was aware of what I was doing I had cut through two layers of abdominal muscle, just shy of breaching the third and final layer. Hot jets of blood squirted into my face and onto my chest, pooling in the small pocket formed by the lower edge of the incision that was longer than my forearm.

My hands were shaking, and I felt a little light-headed, as though any moment I was about to faint or need to sit down. Gore painted my green waterproofs an odd muted scarlet and I had to grit my teeth and take several deep breaths through my flaring nostrils until I had calmed enough to make that final cut, entering the abdominal cavity.

It's just like a cat spay, I mentally cajoled. *Make a snip with the scissors and make sure you don't cut through anything important!*

Yeah… it was exactly like a giant cat spay. I would have laughed at my inner voice if I didn't think it wouldn't come out sounding slightly hysterical.

Thankfully, as I dithered, psyching myself up to do what needed to be done, I heard the sound of a car driving onto the yard and almost dropped to my knees with thankfulness that my moral support had arrived.

Carl walked into the shed, pulling on a floor-length rubber calving gown, as I was beginning my incision through the final layer of abdominal muscle and peritoneum.

"Brilliant," he rubbed his hands together as he saw my progress. "You're almost there. We'll have that calf out in no time."

I gathered he was eager to get back home. Although I had no idea what time of night it was, I knew it had to be late. It had been past half-ten before I'd arrived at the farm myself, and as I'd observed more than once, time seemed to inexplicably speed up when calving cows.

Once he'd scrubbed his hands and arms, Carl moved to my side, helpfully placing his hand in the incision when the small intestine made an ill-thought bid for freedom. I took over as a barricade while he inserted his hand and forearm into the cow's abdomen, grasping for the calf contained within her uterus.

"There's a head," he grunted a little with exertion as he performed feats of contortion that every vet who's ever calved a cow will be intimately familiar with. "And I've got a foot. You're right, Gwen, I doubt you'd have got this thing out by yourself; it's huge!"

A further couple of minutes of persuasion and I saw the off-pink surface of the uterus peek through the layers of muscle and fat.

"Right, make your incision here, over the forelimb," Carl indicated the area he was speaking of with his thumbs as his hands were too busy grappling with the calf. "Use scissors so you don't inadvertently cut the calf. And try to avoid the caruncles, they'll bleed like stink."

With more confidence than I felt I made my cut.

"That ok?" I asked with a shaky voice.

"A bit bigger; he's a big one."

I extended my incision and deposited my scissors on my 'table', ready to give a hand to haul the calf into the world.

The baby slid out of the uterus in a slimy, slippery rush and between the two of us we barely managed to not drop him on the floor. He was big; almost as long as I was tall and very solidly built. There was no way he would have come out the back end.

"I'll grab the uterus," Carl instructed, dipping into the cow's abdomen as the organ attempted to slither away out of reach. "You check whether he's doing ok."

I used my fingernails to tear away the foetal membranes from around his nose and mouth. Grabbing fistfuls of clean straw, I rubbed them briskly over his chest hoping to stimulate his breathing, hoping that we had acted fast enough to ensure he would live.

A hoarse cough and a wet, sloppy shake of his head signalled the calf was going to be alright. Regardless, I replaced the now disgusting, wilted straw with a fresh batch and continued to rub his chest, drying him and making sure we got anything he might have swallowed out of his airway.

A glance over my shoulder revealed Carl efficiently stitching the hole in the uterus, so I re-focused my attention on the calf. I checked its naval to make sure it didn't need tying off and lifted its hind leg to check we were correct in our summation of its sex.

It was a heifer calf.

"He's a she!" I exclaimed with a laugh, and Mr Lightfoot beamed with pleasure.

"She's a gud un," he chortled happily.

Stepping over the calf I went to assist Carl to suture up and faster than I had thought possible, or would ever be able to replicate, the incision was fully closed. I ferried equipment back to my car and fetched anti-inflammatories and antibiotics both to inject and to leave on site to finish off the course. Due to the boot of my estate being so large I had to balance on the bumper to retrieve some of the items I required, and Carl laughed at the sight of me half hanging out of the car with my feet off the ground.

By the time we were all finished and cleared up, I fished my watch out of my pocket and checked the time. It was two o'clock in the morning. All I wanted now was to head home and crawl into bed, but I thought a shower would be a good idea if I didn't want cow on my sheets.

Bidding everyone good night I propped my eyelids open and, mindful of how tired I was, drove very carefully back along the narrow, winding roads until I reached the edges of civilisation. At that point I noticed there was a police car in my rear-view mirror and checked my speedo. I was only going thirty miles an hour, so I wasn't in trouble, and they didn't have the blues and twos on. I figured they were just doing their usual rounds and tried to ignore their presence.

Which would have been a much easier task if they hadn't appeared to be *following* me.

Nervously I pulled up in front of my house, assuming the police car would continue on its way and I wouldn't have anything to worry about. My mind was already on my immediate plan of shower and bed.

Except the police car pulled up alongside me and stopped. The driver's window rolled down and the officer inside motioned for me to wind down my passenger window.

"Um, can I help you?" I asked worriedly. Did I have a light out? Or was there something else wrong with the car? If so, why hadn't they pulled me over?

"Do you mind if we ask you what you're doing, Miss?" the police officer asked, squinting at me somewhat suspiciously.

I bit my lip anxiously and tasted the unmistakable tang of iron. My eyes widened as the realisation that I hadn't bothered to wash my face before leaving the farm slowly percolated through my sleep-deprived brain.

"Um, I've just finished work," I responded awkwardly.

"What were you doing?" came the immediate query.

"I was – uh – calving a cow, a caesarean actually," I stuttered. "I'm a vet."

The two police officers exchanged a disbelieving glance. Obvious they didn't believe me. Just because I'm small and female it doesn't mean that I'm *not* a vet.

"Do you mind if we look in the back of your car, Miss?"

I shook my head and shoved open my door, catching a glimpse of my reflection in the side-mirror and wanting to face-palm with embarrassment. My whole face was covered in scarlet. As were my arms and the collar of my polo-shirt. I walked around the back of the car and saw the bumper was similarly smeared in scarlet gore.

They probably thought I'd murdered someone and stuffed them in the boot to hide the body.

I opened the boot to reveal all of my vet gear and the police officers exchanged another unconvinced glance, but since there was evidently no dead body – there wasn't even *room* for a dead body in the back of my car – they really had no other recourse but to send me on my merry way.

"Very well," the police officer muttered without looking at me. "Carry on."

They climbed back into their car and drove off, leaving me staring after them, wondering whether I had just hallucinated the entire episode. I couldn't even imagine what their conversation was like as they turned the corner at the end of the road. They were probably making a note of my number plate and warning every other squad car in the area about the crazy vet lady with a blood smeared bumper.

Slamming the boot shut I went into my house, had the fastest shower on record and gratefully collapsed face down on my mattress until my alarm clock woke me up a measly four hours later to do Saturday morning surgery.

Such was the life of a vet.

CHAPTER TEN

June equals ... Snow? What?

One morning at the beginning of June I woke up and drew back my curtains to be greeted with the sight of the world covered in a layer of the fluffy, white stuff. My fuzzy, just woke up, not quite functioning as it should be brain gaped at the view from my window and went *What?!*

I rubbed my eyes and blinked, doing a rapid double take, trying to think whether I'd ingested something dubious the night before to make me see things. I couldn't possibly be seeing what I was currently seeing. It couldn't possibly have snowed overnight in June. Could it?

Where I came from it very rarely snowed *at all*, so I really wasn't used to waking up to mornings such as this one. Especially not in *June*.

I had to be hallucinating or have fallen into a coma of some sort in the summer and woken up in winter. Right. *Right?*

I grabbed my phone and dialled Jess' number, wanting confirmation that I was in fact going mad and I should get myself fitted for my own private hug-me suit.

"Hello!" Jess was her usual chipper, cheerful self, even at this ungodly hour of the morning.

That alone made me want to hang up in unbridled disgust. A morning person I was most definitely not, and probably never would be. Anyone who has ever lived with me knew they were unlikely to get much more than a grunt or the occasional growl out of me before breakfast. Trying to solicit intelligible conversation from me was a doomed endeavour. At least it is before I've showered and eaten and had a chance to ease my mind into the day.

"It's snowing," I said, hoping that really it wasn't, and some form of undisclosed chalky accident had occurred outside my house. It could have happened, couldn't it?

"Well good morning to you too," Jess chuckled, knowing from the few times I had been in the practice of a morning early that I functioned at a suboptimal level without food and at least one cup of tea.

"Snow," I said again, bewildered by this turn of events, unable to process the sight in front of my eyes and communicate my dismay at it in any understandable form of sentence.

"Yes, it does that sometimes in this part of the world," she said with perfect unconcern, as though snow at this time of the year was a completely *normal* thing to occur.

"It's June," I reiterated just in case she had missed the point I was trying to make.

"Yup," she sounded way too happy with this awful occurrence. "It happens."

This time I did hang up. I just couldn't cope with cheerful people or this weird microclimate without caffeine.

As I had now been at the practice for nearly three months, I was considered experienced enough by my bosses to take over a couple of the easier routine fertility visits in order to free up some of Andrew's time for other matters. Although that sounded like a far more complicated task than it actually was.

While fertility visits on dairy farms can be overwhelmingly nerve racking and require a lot of skill and the intimate knowledge of a cow's reproductive cycle, those on beef suckler units were much less daunting in comparison. All the beef guys want to know is whether a particular animal is in calf or not, and approximately how many months along they are. As opposed to the dairy routines that generally involve the use of an ultrasound scanner, a foetus the length of my little finger and the demand for a conception date down to within a couple of days accuracy.

No one in their right mind would send a new grad out to do that kind of work, but on a beef herd it was unlikely to send them crying and screaming running for the hills.

My first routine, which was destined to become a regular occurrence during the early summer, was for Mr West at Shieldhall Farm. The farm itself was out in the middle of nowhere and was a nice drive through some very pleasant country. Most importantly, as far as I was concerned, it was very difficult to miss. A bright, white painted sign advertising Shieldhall Limousins pointed me in the right direction and I bumped my way down a long track, carefully avoiding the sheep grazing peacefully on either side. I arrived at a neat and tidy farmyard with well cared for buildings rising up on all sides.

Mr West guided me to park beside the merrily painted farmhouse and came around to my car door as I stepped out.

"You must be Gwen," he said briskly, but not in an unfriendly manner. "I've heard all about you, pet."

"Only good things, I hope!" I replied half-joking, half-serious. I had learned to take everything our farm clients said with a large dose of salt and to give as good as I got. They had mostly been pleasant enough to my face, but I never knew what they were saying between themselves or indeed to Andrew.

Mr West's dark eyes twinkled with a hint of mischief and a small smile graced his bluff, ruddy features. He clapped his hands, rubbing them together with a hearty laugh.

"Ahhh, but that would be tellin'!" he returned, not exactly comfortingly, but I suspected that was his aim. The farmers did very much enjoy a bit of craic. Generally, at my expense.

Getting my gear out of the boot and mentally running through my list of things to bring with me; *lube, arm length gloves, injections should they be needed... Don't forget the needles and syringes!* I followed Mr West over to the shiny new crush set between the buildings. He provided me with a low, folding table to put my bits and pieces on, a rarity on most visits, and I began to understand why I had been sent here in particular to do my first session of pregnancy diagnosis.

In short order Mr West and helper had the first batch of cattle in the collecting yard leading into a high sided race that connected to the crush. A series of movable gates allowed the easy movement and separation of animals, a system that would permit one or two people to organise a large number of stock without stress for animals or handlers, danger or the need for an excessive amount of shouting.

The only problem with this system became apparent when the first cow was secured in the crush by the means of an automatic locking head-yoke, a kick-bar in place and I stepped around behind her, prepared to do my thing.

Except there was no way I was going to reach where I needed to without some very precarious scrambling and creative use of contortionism. The cow herself was fairly tall, and the crush had a small step on it, making the animal even taller still, and I was still only five feet two.

Mr West and Co had a good laugh at the situation for several minutes before he began to make his way over to the workshop.

"I'll get the stepladder," he chortled merrily. "We've never had this problem afore. You must be the shortest vet Andrew's ever employed, petal."

He returned a moment later with, as promised, a small two step stepladder, which he very generously positioned for me in the appropriate place. I climbed it with as much grace and dignity as I could muster and set about my work.

"They say that good things come in small parcels," I returned.

"Aye, that they do, pet," he chuckled. "But then again so does poison! At least you've got nice little hands for lambing, not like the dinner plates some of the other men have to work with."

The majority of my 'pds' that day were pretty simple. There's nothing like inserting a hand into a cow's rectum and meeting her calf for a pat on the head to confirm that she is in calf. Some of them were slightly more difficult, being earlier on in their gestation, some were definitely gelt – not pregnant at all – and there were a couple I had to confess I didn't know, and for a clearer picture ought to be rechecked in a few weeks. Then they would either be further along and easier to feel or there would be no change at all and a definite not in calf. We had always been encouraged at uni that if we didn't know, or weren't completely sure of a pregnancy diagnosis to tell the client, rather than making a mistake and either leaving an animal empty or injecting one with hormone to get her to cycle when she was already pregnant and cause the calf to be lost.

Mr West seemed to appreciate my honesty, and within a few moments had correctly sorted the cattle into groups of in calf, not in calf or don't know, to manage them accordingly. These cattle were scheduled to calve down over the latter portion of the winter while they were still housed, so Mr West could keep a close eye on them in the event that any assistance needed to be rendered. When the cows were put out to pasture in the spring, they would all have large, healthy calves at foot so if there was any adverse weather, as was not unlikely in this part of the world, they would be better able to withstand whatever was thrown at them. Some preferred to defer their calving period until the cattle were no longer housed, meaning their cows calved outside, reducing the stocking density and hopefully reducing the spread of neonatal disease. There were advantages and disadvantages to both systems, but none of them were entirely fool proof.

Mr West and I parted ways happily, him to his dinner and me back to the practice for mine. Three weeks later when I returned to re-examine the few 'maybes' I had pulled out, the stepladder made a repeat appearance and from there on in became fondly known as the Gwen-ladder, complete with its own label and everything.

When I returned to the practice after my first visit to Shieldhall Farm, Carl was just winding up his long list of operations as usual, the kennels full of sleepy, hard-done-by dogs and cats with stitches in various places on their anatomy. A cat carrier had been placed on one of the chairs in the office, although I was unaware that we were expecting any further inpatients, and as I looked at it the carrier rocked gently.

"What's in the box?" I queried as I snagged the farm book, an A4 *black and red* notebook, to write up my calls for the morning.

"A member of the public found a stray kitten on the side of the road up Burnhope way," Leah responded without glancing away from her careful scrutiny of the computer screen, a pair of spectacles perched primly on the bridge of her nose. "Tiny little thing. Doesn't look quite old enough to be away from its mam."

As I was already well on my way to earning the title of mad cat lady – anything fluffy and feline always had my immediate attention – I bent to peer into the cat basket. A small white, tabby and apricot bundle of fur sporting two massive ears and even bigger green eyes stared back at me with shivering concern. A scrawny tail wrapped around a set of dainty white front paws and the little mouth opened wide in a gigantic yawn revealing needle-sharp white teeth and the pale pink shell of the hard palate.

No bigger than the palm of my rather small hands, the scruffy little kitten was evidently no more than four or five weeks old, and kind of cute in a fugly sort of way. Unable to resist, I opened the front of the carrier and scooped the kitten out into the crook of my arm. It maiowed plaintively as I stroked over its knobbly spine, automatically doing a quick parasite check before lifting the tiny creature up to eye level. A soft paddy paw patted my cheek, claws retracted, and a rough pink tongue rasped against the end of my nose.

"Well, aren't you just adorable?" I asked the kitten, checking the sex by lifting the tail and discovering it was a she. I cuddled the kitten again and turned back to Leah. "What's going to happen to her?"

"We couldn't get through to the cat shelter," Leah returned. "So, she'll stay here for the night at least. Carl said we'd probably keep her for a few days in case someone comes looking."

I looked the little cat, nestled comfortably in my bent arm, over again, seeing the signs of lack of care in her straggly coat and low body weight despite the bulging wormy belly. I very much doubted she had someone who would come for her.

"Y'know what?" Jess poked her head around the door, watching me cuddle the kitten with a small, knowing smirk. "You should take her home with you and the cat can teach that beast you call a rabbit some manners!"

"Have you met Cola?" I laughed without rancour at her characterisation of my pet. The rabbit was a nightmare, and I knew it. "Grown men tremble in fear of her. Besides, Himself would kill me."

"It's your house, you can do what you like," Jess continued with a half-hearted scowl, her hands immediately popping onto her hips, striking a combative pose. "And he can sod off if he doesn't like it!"

My boyfriend wasn't the biggest fan of cats as pets. He came from farming stock and believed that cats should live outside and catch rats. As opposed to my family's attitude to our cats which falls just short of Egyptian-like worship. I can assure you I've never yet drawn a picture of my cat on the wall. I always said if reincarnation actually occurred, I wanted to come back as a cat owned by one of my relatives.

"Don't tempt me," I tried to sound severe, but I couldn't help but smile at the kitten purring in my hands. She was rather lovable. Or was that just the mad cat lady in me dying to get out talking?

Knowing I had work to do I put the cat back in its box, but not before snapping a quick photograph of her cuteness to send to my other half with a sad, pleading message. I felt my heartstrings pull at her predicament. If she wasn't claimed by the end of the week she would undoubtedly go to Cat's Protection or an RSPCA rehoming centre, and who knew what would happen to her then. Although as a rule kittens didn't have much of a problem finding a new home. That was the older cats, specifically the black ones, as though people were still wary of black cats being witches' familiars.

By the end of the week the kitten was still with us, looking very fed up and lonely in her kennel. Every time a staff member walked past, she would launch herself at the bars and poke her tiny white paws through in an attempt to grab hold of an item of clothing. *Play with me! Pay attention to me!* Her plaintive miaow would say. The response I received to my pleading message was it was my house and my decision. So, the kitten came to live with me, was renamed Mischief, and spent the first several months of her life being chased around the living room by an angry rabbit half its size.

That little kitten called Mischief very much landed on her feet.

CHAPTER ELEVEN

July and August – L'eau de Crazy

The summer months on farm are generally a season of quiet, of grass growing and mowing and animals getting fat before the winter. In an area of mostly beef cattle and sheep farms this means large animal work usually tapers off during the warmer months, leaving veterinary practices such as Oakbank with time on its hands to reflect on the winter and spring just gone, and prepare for the one to come.

We would have a trickle of what were classed as 'sick cow' calls; a mixture of metabolic or nutritional imbalances and summer mastitis, which were tricky enough of their own accord to require a specific skillset and keep us from getting bored. But we were nowhere near inundated with 'firefighting' emergencies as we had been during the hectic months of lambing and calving season. It was quite a pleasant change of pace all things considered. It would be impossible to keep up with that level of intense daily calls and out of hours all year around without utterly burning out by the end of a twelvemonth.

This was the time of year where habitually the vets took their holidays. We were encouraged to take three weeks off in the summer, generally in a run-on block, and then a further week in the weeks leading up to Christmas. To cover these holiday periods, and ensure the remaining vets were not completely rushed off their feet, a locum veterinary surgeon was always employed, saving the sanity of everyone involved. That first summer our locum was a very pleasant chap from Scotland called Len, who came complete with gorgeous rescue dog and intrepid three-legged cat called Mo.

Often when I arrived for work in the morning I would encounter Mo waiting at the door to the flat, having made an emergency evac from the upstairs window due to whatever convoluted twist of feline logic occurred to him at the time, but not being capable of returning inside via the same route due to his lacking a fourth limb. If he had been my cat, I would have been terrified of losing him, or him getting hurt in an unfamiliar environment, but Len did not seem similarly concerned. As the pet of a locum, Mo must have been very used to upping sticks and moving house every few weeks or months, and was, I supposed, quite familiar with finding his way around new and varied places of residence.

Locum vets are an excellent opportunity for new graduates, as they generally bring with them a wealth of experience and techniques learned from the different practices they have been to. If, as a young vet, it was possible to pick their brains for advice, it was always a good thing to do so, albeit treading that find line between being curious, and becoming an annoyance. I learned a great deal from Len that I otherwise might not have come across, working with only two other vets, and he was a jolly, congenial sort of person into the bargain, a general must have for anyone trying to fit into an already established practice environment.

July into August of 2012 was a funny old summer. The weather, for the first time in years, was utterly sublime. It was the best season I could remember for a very long time when the sun shone for the majority of the time and the little bit of rain that did fall was a welcome relief. Consultation-wise things were not necessarily so joyous.

With Carl the first of us to take his three-week break, I was designated his replacement in the operating theatre. Thankfully everyone else had decided to take it easy on me, as I was still relatively slow and uncertain regarding surgery. Only a mere fraction of the operations Carl would plough through in a week were scheduled for me to be getting on with, although as far as I was concerned there were plenty enough. During the spring I had been doing a steady stream of cat speys and castrates, lump removals and, on quiet days, one or two bitch speys, closely supervised so if anything unexpected happened there was always someone on hand to save the day, should it be required. I was well prepared for my stint as the operating vet for the next handful of weeks, and looking forward to the opportunity to improve and expand my skills, despite the tickley nervous feeling in my stomach that spoke of a healthy dose of trepidation at the prospect of the responsibility.

It was perfectly okay to feel a hint of anxiety, I told myself, gazing at my reflection in my bathroom mirror the first morning of Carl's absence. There was always some risk involved with any surgical procedure, any *anaesthetic*, regardless of the age or health of the animal in question. There was always a hint of uncertainty about how the animal would respond to this drug or that drug, especially if they had never had anything done before. Even if they had already undergone some form of surgery in the past there was no guarantee *this* one would be equally as smooth sailing.

Something that generally members of the public didn't seem to realise is many of the operations we perform as almost *routine* were actually very major, very difficult surgeries. Take a bitch spey for example; it is in actual fact major abdominal surgery, going in and removing an entire organ system. We have to contend with the large veins that supply said organ safely and securely, and yet it is what we as a profession classify as a 'year one skill'; something a fresh new graduate straight out of vet school ought to be competent to achieve within their first few nerve-wracking months of practice.

I knew some vets who utterly despised bitch speys, who would beg, barter or steal to avoid having to do one, even ten years down the line.

Thankfully I was not completely alone in theatre. I had a very good, very skilled and very efficient nursing staff to give me encouragement, monitor anaesthetics, so I didn't have to worry about how *that* was going, as well as concentrate on surgery, and chivvy me along in an attempt to keep me to some kind of time. And Len was there as well to often lend a hand in his, laidback, unruffled manner. Even when I had a stubborn bleeding vessel I just couldn't reach, or get a sufficient ligature on, he would amble into theatre, do his thing and everything would be alright again.

But although I found the surgery taxing and it stretched my brain and skills until I was exhausted by the end of each morning, it was not operating that was the oddest or most vexing part of the summer. That honour fell to the owner of a very nice Staffordshire Bull Terrier called Dotty.

Dotty belonged to a Polish immigrant by the name of Mr Kowalczyk. He was an elderly gentleman, whose age I had never been quite able to accurately determine, although I was certain it fell between sixty and eighty. He had longish, unkempt, straggly greyish hair, slightly balding on the top, an attempt at a beard and rather thin, suspicious features. He reminded me a little of *Boris the Blade* from the film *Snatch*. But then again, I'm a huge movie fan and the majority of life reminds me in some way or another of a film.

Mr Kowalczyk became my client courtesy of Andrew, who, despite his usual easy-going demeanour, disliked the man with almost religious fervour and couldn't stand to be in the same room as him for longer than a few minutes before he cracked and an argument ensued.

"The joys of being the low man in the totem pole, I'm sorry to say," Andrew said with manically grinning glee as he pointed out the appointment before morning surgery began. "And it is sort of your own fault. You're the one with l'eau de Crazy."

Ever since that fateful battle with a Chihuahua called Pico, Andrew and Carl had designated me as their go-to person for the practice's more eccentric clientele, especially as – despite my being convinced she thought I'd tried to murder her beloved dog – Ms Dalfour asked for *me* every time she came back for a consultation. To the detriment of my hands and fingers. Apparently, I had more patience than both of them combined, plus a very good poker-face – which Andrew repeatedly tried to disrupt by lying in wait for me in the dispensary while I was consulting and launching appropriate Monty Python quotes in my direction, trying to make me crack. It had become something of a competition between us, and I think it amused him to see me desperately trying to keep a straight face. In another example of how truly warped most vets are we all three fought over who got to see cat bite abscesses and similar ilk, even going so far as to run the length of the practice to make sure we were the first to call that particular client in. Every vet I'd ever met liked the satisfaction of squeezing a good, juicy abscess.

In any event, Andrew and Carl had affectionately decided I must have some kind of perfume that attracted the more unconventional of our clients and had christened it my *l'eau de Crazy*. I didn't really mind, although sometimes my collection of crazies just about drove me up the walls.

Enter stage left Mr Kowalczyk, one bright, hot July morning.

As I didn't have a hope of ever pronouncing his name correctly, I was grateful the pet had an easy name, and did the old veterinary trick of when unsure of a client's surname call them in by their animal. Mr Kowalczyk marched determinedly inside, dragging a reluctant Dotty in his wake, immediately taking a seat on the windowsill of the wide open sash window. It was about twenty-six degrees in my consulting room, an unbearable, sweltering heat that threatened to have me melting on the spot, and as the building pre-dated air-conditioning by several decades the best we could do was an open window, closed whenever the patient was of the feline persuasion, and a struggling desk fan. However, whenever a client sat on the windowsill, I couldn't help but cringe at the vision of the window coming crashing down on them.

"It is feet," Mr Kowalczyk barked in a harsh, staccato accent unsullied by the years he had undoubtedly spent on English soil. He scowled at me from dark, piercing, sparrow-like eyes. "She biting them all time. I clean but she bite still, all times."

He bent and picked up poor Dotty's front foot, whether she wanted to give it to him or not and practically thrust it at me, spreading her toes to reveal the reddened, irritated webs between. Getting onto my knees beside the very much unimpressed Staffie, I held out my hand for possession of the offending foot.

"May I?" I asked and he seemingly reluctantly relinquished it to my grasp. Patting Dotty sympathetically I gently manipulated her paw, examining the areas between her toes that were wet, inflamed and puffy. "Is it only this one foot she's having a problem with?"

"You have to speak up," Mr Kowalczyk practically shouted, pointing at the clear, plastic hearing aids in both ears his lank coiffeur had previously hidden. "I have hearing aid."

I repeated my question at a louder volume and he vigorously shook his head.

"Has on all feet!" he proclaimed loudly, bending once again to pick up her other three unmolested feet to demonstrate his words.

True to his claims all four feet did display the offending swellings, which helpfully removed a grass seed foreign body from my list of differential diagnoses. Dotty gave a long-suffering sigh, and I patted her a second time.

"I think I know what the problem is here," I said in a slightly louder tone than my normal speaking voice and feeling a little ridiculous for it. "These little lumps between her toes are cysts. They usually happen if the feet have been irritated by something they have come into contact with, or if the dog has an allergy, have you-"

Mr Kowalczyk's dark eyes lit up and he interrupted before I had the chance to ask how long he had owned the dog and whether it had happened before. Generally, an allergy to something in the environment appeared on a seasonal basis if it was related to vegetation or remained all year 'round if it was something more ubiquitous. Like house dust mites or fungus.

"My neighbour, he try to poison, Dotty!" he exclaimed with all the violent conviction of the zealous. "He put chemical on drive where Dotty walk. I tell him not, but he not listen, so I wash feet, now this happen!"

I suspected it was more likely due to the constant washing, and not properly drying, than anything his neighbour had used to clean his drive, but I bit the inside of my mouth hard to stop myself from voicing my opinion. I really didn't want to get into an argument with him right now about whether or not his neighbour was poisoning his dog.

"Well, it *could* be because she has stepped in a chemical," I said cautiously, feeling as though I was chewing my words and hoping they wouldn't be used to bludgeon his neighbours into submission later. "But it could also be due to something else in the environment, like grasses or tree pollen, or even her diet."

There are myriad reasons a dog could form interdigital cysts such as these; too many to even think about, never mind try to discuss with my client who was viewing me with a thunderous, judgemental frown. Before he could open his mouth to begin another diatribe about someone trying to poison poor, long-suffering Dotty, I continued my summation of the problem.

"These cysts have become infected," I gave one of the purplish discoloured, bloated blobs a gentle squeeze, and was rewarded with a satisfying rush of bloody pus and another sigh from Dotty. "So, Dotty will need a course of antibiotics, and something to take away the itch."

The most common anti-inflammatory, anti-itch product used in veterinary medicine is systemic steroid. Unfortunately, our patients are not particularly ideal candidates for hydrocortisone creams, as it's impossible to explain to them they mustn't lick the cream off, without an elaborate contrivance with socks and tape, or an

Elizabethan collar to keep their mouths away from the affected areas. Despite some side effects, steroids *are* very effective at preventing an animal from causing self-trauma due to itching, and also, perhaps most importantly with many clients, they are incredibly cheap. Unlike with the National Health Service, veterinary medicine is not free at the point of service, and even if an animal is insured, we constantly have to keep one eye on cost, and way-up the cost-benefit ratio before deciding what can be prescribed to whom.

"If you are going to wash her feet, you must make sure you dry them properly," I continued. "Allowing her feet to stay damp is going to make the problem worse; so, make sure her feet are dry after she comes back from a walk, and also try to stop her from licking at them. You can try to put socks on her when you're not going to be with her, if you think she won't eat them that is."

I really didn't want to solve one problem, only to have precipitated a situation whereby Dotty had to have an operation to remove a sock lodged in her intestines. It wasn't an uncommon occurrence for dogs to eat items of clothing, balls, stones or toys and for them to have to be physically removed from the gut by way of an expensive and complicated surgery.

"I wash her feet," Mr Kowalczyk seemed to perk up a little at this instruction, and I wondered whether he had understood anything I had just told him, or if he just hadn't been listening. "And make sure dry them."

"Yes," I tried not to mirror Dotty's sigh. "I'll just be a moment and get her medication."

I ducked out into the dispensary with some relief, only to find Andrew waiting for me with an eager, expectant, boyish expression on his face. He was enjoying this far too much.

"You owe me lots of chocolate for this," I accused in a low voice as I contemplated the groaning shelves in search of the appropriate drugs. "He thinks his neighbour is poisoning the dog."

Andrew actually had the nerve to laugh.

"He's a cherry short of a fruitcake."

I growled at him, collected my medications and returned to my consulting room. Once through the door I plastered my pleasant smile back on my face and presented the prescription to the client.

"So she needs one of these antibiotics twice daily for a week, with or without food, it doesn't matter," I handed Mr Kowalczyk a paper envelope containing a blister-strip of fourteen tablets. A pill bottle containing seven white tablets followed. "And one of these *once* daily, again, with or without food, it doesn't matter. And we'll re-examine Dotty in a week."

Mr Kowalczyk's expression didn't change as he took his medications and shuffled out of the consulting room to the reception hatch where he made his repeat appointment and grumbled about the price of his treatment, before pulling a fat roll of twenties from his pocket and handing over the appropriate amount. His poor dog sat at his feet with a graceless flop, giving a high-pitched Staffie whine, evidently more than used to his combative outlook on life.

The next week, Dotty was back in my consulting room, her feet looking much more comfortable, but her expression remained utterly morose.

"I tell my neighbour," Mr Kowalczyk repeated for what felt like the thousandth time in the space of ten minutes. "Dotty's feet *his* fault, but he ignore me! I put socks on to protect feet when we go walking…" he produced a set of small, white baby socks from his pockets and showed them to me almost proudly. Dotty continued to pant like a train, no change there then… "I say *here Dotty put on socks and we go out.*"

"Her feet are doing very well," I acknowledged the obvious and tried not to look at the clock. My Kowalczyk was proving unusually chatty this week and I was certain I was now running behind, but I couldn't think of a polite way to get rid of him. "She doesn't need to continue with the antibiotics as the cysts have cleared up nicely, but I think we'll keep her on a lower dose of the steroid for at least another week."

A second week passed and Dotty was once again back in my consulting room. There was absolutely nothing wrong with her feet that I could see, but I had discovered Mr Kowalczyk appeared to like to talk to me. Possibly almost as much as he appeared to enjoy arguing over the bill. I wondered whether he was lonely. It wasn't uncommon for elderly pet owners who lived alone to come to the vets more for the human contact than because of any pressing concern about their animal.

"And I have hernia you see," he made as though he was going to show me the problem in question and I thought my head was about to explode, uttering a quick demurral before he could reveal anything that might scar me for life. I was a vet for a reason, I didn't do people. "It makes it difficult to put sock on and off, and bend to wash feet."

"Well, I think we can stop using the socks," I said, hoping if I talked then maybe he might not attempt to show me anymore of his own ailments. "And finish the steroids. Just keep an eye on her, and we'll see her again if there is any reoccurrence."

A fortnight later, Dotty was in my consulting room with sore feet. Or at least sore feet according to her owner.

The skin between her toes was perhaps a little pinker than the rest of her skin, and that was only evident on very close inspection, but there was no evidence of any further cystic developments. There was no infection, and stoical Dotty gave no indication that my poking and prodding of her apparently uncomfortable appendages was troubling to her.

"She very sore," Mr Kowalczyk insisted when I told him I couldn't find anything particularly untoward upon examination. "Very lame. We walk on grass all time, and she chew feet when we get home every day."

I suspected Dotty had a grass allergy but was reluctant to give a three year old dog a prolonged course of steroids if I could possibly help it. There were a few other options for allergic dogs; either a cyclosporine immune-modulatory drug licensed in dogs, or blood sampling to find out exactly what she was allergic to and then make up a vaccine to control her response to those particular allergens. But both of them were almost prohibitively expensive to pets that were not insured, of which Dotty was one. I doubted Mr Kowalczyk, who quibbled over paying a few pounds for a week or two of steroid tablets was going to agree to fork out at least a couple of hundred pounds for the other options.

I gave Dotty some antihistamines and Mr Kowalczyk bought her some dog booties to protect her feet from the grass pollen. As a treatment it was perhaps not the most effective, but it kept the client happy, and the animal as comfortable as I could manage in this particular situation.

I have learned since graduating that although veterinary medicine was about treating the problem presented to me, it was also vitally important to manage the client's expectations. If a client was expecting a particular medication to completely cure the problem, and it didn't, they would undoubtedly go away upset, or disillusioned and potentially move to another practice. Clear communication and succinct explanations were of utmost importance between client and veterinary surgeon, almost as important as the actual application of medication.

Part of me wished I had paid far more attention in my communication skills lectures. Or that that particular subject was presented in a more engaging and thought-provoking manner, making me *want* to be involved in the lecture or discussion, rather than just waiting for it to *finally* end.

Unfortunately, poor Dotty, regardless of how effective or not my communication skills were, was destined to become a regular fixture in my consulting room over the course of that long, hot summer. Whether I wanted to or not, I invariably seemed to see her at least on a weekly basis, with her troublesome feet and her hypochondriac owner. Sometimes I wasn't even entirely sure her feet *were* bothering her, or if this was just a case of Mr Kowalczyk having too much time on his hands to stare at his dog, and every minute shift in facial expression, or innocuous lick at a paw, was translated as immense discomfort.

Not even my three-week absence on holiday could make Mr Kowalczyk defect to another vet. While I was away, Len drew the short straw in having to deal with the increasingly grumpy old man, and very merrily passed him back over to *me* when he was preparing to leave.

"He's utterly cracked," our locum informed me cheerfully. "And he's all yours! Have fun with that."

Eventually, as summer was drawing to a close, I managed to convince Mr Kowalczyk to invest in some further diagnostic testing to determine the source of Dotty's foot issue once and for all. Or at least to rule allergies in or out. Blood was taken and sent to the appropriate laboratory, the results returning about a week later. And finally… an answer.

Dotty was indeed allergic to several types of grass pollen, plus a few species of trees and weeds. I felt a certain sense of vindication that I had been correct right from the beginning of this saga. No one had tried to poison Dotty at all; she just had the dog version of hay-fever. Inconvenient and frustrating to attempt to get on top of, but ultimately nothing serious or life-threatening.

Mr Kowalczyk was informed of the results, and a long discussion ensued, lasting the course of several weeks as to what he wanted to do to treat Dotty's allergies. Obviously antihistamines were not quite sufficient to keep the reaction at bay – this wasn't truly a surprise as antihistamine can be very unreliable in dogs – and we were reluctant to give her steroids for any considerable length of time. We had to not just take into account her current levels of comfort, but what the medication might do to her systemically over a prolonged period, which might ultimately culminate in the shortening of her life-span due to the steroid's effect on her liver and kidneys.

I felt as though I was trying to get blood out of a stone, or beating my head against a brick wall until my brain was bruised and battered. My frustration with our stubborn client often manifested itself in me walking into the kennel room after a consultation and screaming, because telling the client to his face how irritating and annoying he was being was just not done. Finally, after seemingly endless visits, back and forth discussions, and enough chocolate ice-cream to drown in, we came to an agreement; Dotty would go on immunotherapy vaccine.

Hallelujah!

After wrangling with the irritation of applying for a special import certificate for the vaccine, which came from a lab in France, and an initial course of weekly injections, I finally seemed to have my consulting room back. Dotty would return once a month for her vaccine injection, and as the summer season faded into autumn we seemed to have managed to get a handle on her tricky feet.

Although how much that was due to the vaccine, and how much was down to the fact the grasses, trees and weeds were no longer producing pollen, we would have to wait until next summer to find out.

I was just grateful I no longer had to listen to Mr Kowalczyk complain about his hernia, his cardiac consultant, and, as ever, his neighbour.

CHAPTER TWELVE

September means Sheep disease

September came upon us like the roaring of a lion with loud cacophonous voice. And yet it was not the weather, which remained pleasantly warm and calm, that provoked such general disharmony, or the dread shadows of long memories and dark dismal days, but the fearsome enemy of every farmer since the time stock first began to be domesticated; infectious disease.

In this part of the country the legacy of Foot and Mouth is still a fresh scar over a poorly healed wound. It can be easily seen in the unused milking parlours and the old flyers still hanging in the vet's office and waiting room advocating an awareness of mental health among the rural community. The majority of the practice's farm clients had lost everything as the disease made its way down the A68 across the Pennines and into neighbouring Cumbria, from auctions and collecting centres. I remember the pyres of dead animals and the noxious, lingering stink of burning flesh from when the epidemic struck Lancashire, and I knew what I had experienced was but a drop in the ocean compared to what the farmers who were wiped out and vets who were responsible for the culls went through. Some of them never recovered.

It all began one bright, sunny Monday morning, when Andrew took a trip out to the middle of nowhere to see a tup with a lump on its jaw. This was the time of year when an illness or injury to any of the male breeding sheep on a farm was a pressing, immediate concern, as any problems now could lead to him becoming sub, or completely infertile during the period over the next couple of months when the ewes went to the tup with the expectation of lambs in late winter and spring. A male with poor fertility could lead to a smaller than anticipated lamb-crop the following year, and potentially erase any profit that particular farm could expect to make. Which was why everyone in the industry took the health of their tups very seriously.

The tup in question did indeed have lump.

Examining a male sheep is no joke. Some of the breeds, of which this particular animal was a Texel, can weigh well over 100kg, and are, as a rule, of a stubborn, determined disposition, with a deep-seated dislike of veterinary interventions. Texels are a squat, somewhat pugnacious-looking breed, and even attempting to wrestle with one is very much like trying to move a quarry block. I generally left the wrangling to the experts and watched from the side lines until my patient was suitably subdued. This of course, sometimes entailed chasing the desired sheep around a field until it collapsed from exhaustion.

I did not envy Andrew his task that morning

He returned bearing a fistful of blood tubes and a grim expression. The lump, it turned out, was not *just* a lump. It was an abscess of a superficial lymph node of the head in a sheep that was far less fit than it really should have been for the time of year.

This is where experience shows. A new graduate such as myself might have been inclined to overlook this discovery as, well, an abscess; easily treated with lancing and a course of penicillin. Andrew knew better. He elected to examine several of the other tups housed with the sick animal and discovered a number of these also had lumps.

At this point alarm-bells would have been going off in his head. This was a typical sign of a disease of sheep and goats called Caseous Lymphadenitis. This condition is caused by the bacterium *Corynebacterium pseudotuberculosis* and causes abscesses in the lymph nodes and lungs of the infected animals, leading to a gradual wasting of condition. It is most commonly transmitted during shearing; by cross contamination of infected material, or by close contact of animals leading to respiratory disease. Flocks of sheep endemically infected with caseous lymphadenitis produce poorer quality fleeces and have a significant increase in condemning of carcases at slaughter leading to a reduction in overall profitability of the enterprise.

A simple blood sample would tell us whether this really was a case of CLA, and then the real hard work would ensue.

A week later we had the results of the blood sample, and it was not happy news. Four out of the five samples Andrew had taken were confirmed positive for CLA, meaning our client had a much larger problem than he had initially thought. Now we would have to embark upon a vast amount of testing to discover the true scope of the infection and whether it was solely among his tups, or whether it had managed to get into the 1800 ewes currently two months shy of their breeding season.

It was a vast number of sheep to blood test and guess who inevitably got stuck with the majority of the donkey-work... me. That's not to say I didn't have help, but I spent the next week bleeding a couple of thousand sheep.

That first morning of testing I arrived at Burnfield Farm a nervous wreck. I had never done much blood sampling of sheep before, and although I knew the theory behind it, I also knew how truly difficult it could be. Sheep had a small band of muscle next to the jugular that sometimes served to conceal the vein from the vet looking to put a needle into it. Added to this jeopardy was the pressure of ensuring that not too many blood tubes were wasted due to ineffective usage of vacutainer. A Vacutainer blood collection tube is a sterile glass or plastic tube with a closure that is evacuated to create a vacuum inside the tube facilitating the draw of a predetermined volume of liquid. Once perforated it would not draw blood and was thus useless. The trick was to insert the needle into the vein, ensure blood was indeed on the other side, before puncturing the seal, which is all in all easier said than done.

This work would require a staggering number of needles and blood tubes, and I was suitably daunted by the scope of what I was about to be faced with. The boxes and boxes of equipment alone were incredibly intimidating.

Over the summer months I had grown more and more confident in my ability to succeed as a veterinary surgeon. My knowledge was good, my client interaction improving with every consultation and I was pleased with the steady progression of my clinical skills, all of which I had been forced to document in nauseating detail for a programme of post-graduate review called *Professional Development Phase*, a daily annoyance I overall had little time or inclination to think about. But the prospect of this latest challenge threatened to make my knees knock. An inability to successfully draw blood would lead to a very slow completion of my task and would undoubtedly not reflect well on *me*. It would not take long for my failures to do the rounds of the local community and I would forever be known as *that lady vet who can't get blood outa a sheep*.

The management system on this farm was pretty good; a group of animals would be penned into a race and a series of gates were utilised to separate them out and catch them for examination, or in this case blood drawing. I had plenty of helpers to help make light work of catching and tipping the sheep, but that first fifty animals was a brutal, uphill struggle that had nothing to do with the sheep or the race system or my helpers. It was *me*. I was the problem.

Nerves did not make for a steady hand, and it was taking me several minutes and at least a couple of blood tubes per sheep to get a good enough sample to send away to the lab. If we continued on this way it would be Christmas before we finished sampling the entire flock.

I could feel the eyes of the farmer, a thin, loquacious man I liked a great deal, burning into me with what felt like the fire of a thousand judgemental suns. His entertaining chatter became less and less the longer and longer I struggled until there was only silence and the brisk shouts of the farm hands to one another as they sorted animals. My knees and back were hurting from constantly bending and squatting to draw blood and I felt like I wanted to cry, all of my hard-won confidence draining through my fingers like a handful of sand.

This was hard work, made even harder by the steady stream of unhelpful thoughts that scrolled over the inside of my skull.

I can't do this. God I can't do this. How many vacutainers did it take to draw that sample? Three? Three! Andrew is going to kill me for wasting so much money. They all think I'm utterly useless. What made me think I could do this? I can't do this!

I was starting to work myself into a fine internal lather when I hit a vein on the first try. It was the fiftieth, or the sixtieth sheep through the race, I couldn't remember how long I had been suffering through this torture, but it felt like a lifetime and I stared at the dark, red liquid filling my tube with something akin to astonishment.

It's a Leicester, you'd have to be blind and stupid to miss THAT vein, my snide inner voice retorted, but the success bolstered my rapidly failing confidence and I thought maybe I wasn't as useless as I had initially thought.

Yes, there is a marked difference between the slim, relatively non-fatty neck of a Leicester and the stout, stumpy, almost non-existent neck of a Texel, but it was still an achievement.

The next sheep went the same as the last and I felt my stomach jump with jubilant excitement, really having to try hard to suppress my urge to fist-pump in triumph. This tup was a Suffolk; less stocky than a Texel, but still a meatier customer than the previous Leicester.

Three more successes followed rapidly, one of them including my Texel nemesis, and I could feel myself falling into an efficient rhythm of thought and action.

"Looks like you're on a roll there, pet," Mr Forrester said, after such a long period of silence the sound of his voice almost made me jump.

I glanced up at him, his eyes no longer the burning orbs of fiery judgement they had once appeared – and I now doubted they had ever been – unable to suppress of quick, victorious grin.

"Now we're cooking on gas!" I exclaimed. "Come on; bring on the sheep!"

The one hundred mark rolled by while I was still riding the high of my successes and I suspect the sense of accomplishment I felt was vastly overblown, but this was yet another skill I had mastered and I was inordinately proud of myself.

One hundred and fifty came and went. *Get in!* I inwardly cheered, far more excited than the situation warranted. I talked and laughed with Mr Forrester as he told me about the scraps and scrapes his children were getting themselves into, merrily responding with a number of my own more interesting experiences at vet school.

Two hundred and fifty rolled around. Now it was starting to get tedious. I glanced at my watch seeing that it was barely eleven o'clock and letting out a distinctly deflated sigh. We had begun just shy of half past eight in the morning and now my thighs and back were screaming at me to stand up, just for a moment. I wondered whether I would ever be able to straighten my spine ever again, understanding now why so many of my elders in this profession complained of back problems. This kind of work was brutal on the body, remaining in one position for such a length of time, bending over and standing up. It was pure hell.

The next time someone tried to tell me my job wasn't that strenuous I was going to make them do this and see how they liked it.

As the three hundred and fiftieth sheep was released Mr Forrester consulted his watch and announced it was twelve-thirty; dinnertime.

Hallelujah! I wanted to shout it out loud, but just about refrained from giving voice to my relief.

It was a struggle to get to my feet and Mr Forrester had a good laugh at my expense as I had to use the gate to aid me. Placing my hands on my hips I bent over backward until my spine cracked, vertebrae realigning with a satisfying sense of release. I was utterly exhausted already, and I knew I had entire afternoon to go yet. A groan escaped my tightly clamped lips at the very thought. When I had envisioned what the most physically taxing part of my job would be, I always pictured trying to untwist a uterine torsion, or calving a monstrous calf. I had never really considered how much of a punishment on the body this sort of work could be.

Stripping off my wellies, over-trousers and parlour top at the front door of the farmhouse I gratefully flopped into a chair at the kitchen table, a mug of strong tea immediately placed in front of me. I was completely parched and attacked it with gusto, almost instantaneously regretting it as the scalding liquid burned the roof of my mouth.

"There, flower," Mr Forrester's mother patted my shoulder in a grandmotherly fashion as she furnished me with a much-appreciated glass of water and a plate of absolutely divine smelling shepherd's pie with loads of cheesy mash. "You look done in. Get a bitta food inter ya, pet."

"Thank you, Mrs Forrester," I answered, eagerly awaiting everyone else to take their seats before I dived head-first into my meal. "This looks and smells amazing, I can't wait to try it."

Finally, the rest of the men were seated, I picked up my cutlery and attacked the food with the enthusiasm of a starving dog. I have always had a healthy appetite and the ability to pack away a startling amount in one sitting, despite my smaller frame and stature, something that often shocked people. I finished my first plate of food before the majority of the others at the table had made their way through two-thirds of their portions and glanced up to find them all staring at me with some degree of bemusement. Realising I had just inhaled my food, and it was kind of rude I offered my companions a slight smile.

"I'm sorry, I was really hungry, and this is really good."

"I like a girl with a good appetite," Mrs Forrester said happily, picking up the pan with the remaining pie left in it. "Do ya want seconds?"

I looked at the rest of the table.

"Only if no one else wants any."

"Have at it," Mr Forrester waved his fork in the direction of the pan.

"Then yes please!"

Another heaped spoon of decadent shepherd's pie was placed on my plate, and just as eagerly consumed. A wonderful portion of apple crumble and custard followed the main meal and I sat back in my chair with a feeling of pleasant fullness. Now, if only I didn't have to go back outside and blood sample several hundred more sheep my day would be complete.

"That was some eatin'," Mr Forrester commented as we made our way back toward the race about half an hour later. "I wouldn't ha' thought a slip of a thing like you would manage tha' much."

"It was really good food," I returned happily. "And I was *really* hungry."

By six o'clock we had managed to make our way through eight hundred sheep, and I was beginning to feel broken. As night was beginning to draw in, I decided to call it a day. I would be back in the morning to pick up where we had left off, if I was capable of moving at all that is, and I was hoping that we would manage to finish off the remaining numbers in a single day.

I made my way back to the practice to make sure the bloods I had taken that day were appropriately stored and to clean my equipment before heading home.

"We thought you'd got lost!" Leah jokingly exclaimed when I appeared in reception in search of the paperwork belonging to these samples. "How many did you get through?"

"Eight hundred in all," I responded wearily as I sank boneless into the chair opposite her. "And I don't think I'll ever stand properly again. I'm hoping I'll get through the rest of them tomorrow."

"That's good going!" she returned, throwing a red Quality Street – my favourite – in my direction. "You definitely deserve a chocolate for that!"

I happily put the gooey, chocolatey treat in my mouth and chewed, sighing at the sense of relief the sweet sent coursing through my body. I really should try to wean myself off my monstrous chocolate addiction, but I enjoyed it far too much to even make the attempt.

"Andrew thinks he'll be free to take over if you want him to," Leah continued. "Or you can both go up together and get through them quicker."

"That'd be amazing!" I understood why Andrew hadn't been able to help me today; he had to do the routine at one of our few dairy farms, and then examine several sick cows, one of which had a displaced abomasum, requiring surgery. We had both had a very busy day.

The next day was much of the same, but with Andrew present the job went nearly three times as quickly. We struck up a competition between us, seeing who could bleed the most sheep in the shortest period of time, the farm hands divvying up between the two of us and rowdily cheering us on. Unsurprisingly Andrew won, but those thousand sheep went quickly enough and we were back in the practice sorting our samples by mid-afternoon.

My spine and thighs were very grateful for the reprieve, ready to worship at the altar of whoever had ordained the end of this ordeal.

Once the samples were sent away, we had a week to relax before the toughest part of this process began. Because of the financial impact of this disease, its insidious nature and the difficultly of treatment, the only real way of getting on top of it was to cull the animals that tested positive, and then institute a rigorous segregation and hygiene policy on farm. And then test again the following year. Although the blood test was relatively specific; meaning it was good at detecting the proportion of animals in a group who were truly *negative* for the disease, no test for CLA had good specificity *and sensitivity*. It could be used as the basis of a flock eradication plan, but it would not necessarily pick out every animal that was positive for the infection.

Thankfully, Mr Forrester's situation was not as dire as it could have been. Although roughly ten percent of his flock returned as test positive, it was not as vast a number as we had been afraid it would be. Those sheep that were infected with CLA were rounded up and loaded onto trailers to be taken to the slaughter house for culling.

I felt awful, both for our client, and for myself. It was a terrible feeling to have to inform a farmer he needed to cull a significant proportion of his stock, his livelihood, without receiving any financial compensation for the loss.

He then needed to decide if he wanted to restock the numbers or lamb a smaller flock that year. Both came with their own problems. Adding a large number of animals to his flock at this point in the season would undoubtedly lead to stress, which might result in lowered fertility in his breeding ewes. This in itself could cause a reduction in his conception rates and a small lamb-crop in the next year, despite having similar numbers as he would have before the cull.

I didn't envy him that difficult decision.

This was my first professional brush with infectious disease on a whole flock basis, and it left a particularly bad taste in my mouth.

What made it worse was that Mr Forrester had no idea where the infection had come from, and in a year's time we would have to do it all again. And we might discover we hadn't got it all. We might still need an even larger cull.

This job was not all puppies and kittens. Sometimes we had to make hard decisions and deliver bad news that affected the livelihoods of our clients. And it was not a good feeling.

A week and a half later I went to Mr West's farm to look at a sick sterk; a catch-all description of an animal older than a calf but younger than an adult with no gender specification, depending on which part of the country you happened to be in. The beast was down on its side in a byer, looking as though it was not long for this world. It was blowing like a racehorse at the end of a championship sprint, its membranes a disconcerting blueish colour visible from several feet away.

"It jest went down reet fast," Mr West scratched his head worriedly, deep lines carved around his eyes as he pondered the sick, distressed animal. "A reet good heirfer she is as well, I've given it a coupla shots, but it ain't done a thing."

I climbed into the pen, my trusty stethoscope draped around my neck, and approached the undoubtedly very sick animal. My usual clinical examination of any breed or species began at the mouth and worked its way backward to ensure I didn't miss anything vital. As soon as I opened this sterk's mouth to take a look inside, I felt almost physically sick.

Its mucous membranes were ulcerated, large vesicles, small fluid-filled swellings, lined its gums, and when I gripped its tongue the whole surface of the organ sloughed off in my hand.

I didn't even have the breath to swear as I practically leapt on its feet. If the sterk had similar vesicles on its feet, then we were all in a great deal of trouble. My mind was still stuck on the recent discovery of CLA and the harm infectious disease could cause, and I really didn't want to be that vet who missed Foot and Mouth disease when it came back.

The feet were clear of vesicles, but I couldn't be sure I wasn't missing something. Mr West looked at me as though he thought I'd gone utterly insane.

"It has mouth lesions," I informed him tersely to explain my unusual acrobatics. His mouth formed a shocked 'o' of understanding, even as his ruddy features paled to a sickly grey. He, like me, wanted this to be Foot and Mouth in the same way neither of us wanted a hole in the head. "But nothing on the feet, thank God. I'm going to call Andrew."

I was glad that my employer picked up his phone after only the third ring.

"Mr West's sterk has lesions in its mouth," I said in favour of any polite greetings. I knew I sounded abrupt and rude, but I was panicking too much to think about the consequences of speaking to my boss in such a manner. My stomach felt as though it was lodged in my throat and any moment my breakfast would make an unwelcome reappearance.

Andrew swore long and with creative variety, some of his imprecations I had never even heard before.

"What are its feet like?" he asked just as abruptly, and I heard the sharp bite of worry in his tone. Having seen the worst once in his career it wasn't difficult to evoke the concern it would happen all over again. "Is it the only one?"

"Feet are clean," I informed him and then repeated his question to our worried client. "Mr West says it's the only one like this. The rest of his stock are fine."

"Oh thank God for that!" Andrew's relief exploded from him like a bullet from a gun, making the phone line between us buzz loudly. "You did the right thing in calling, Gwen, but if it's only the one, then it's unlikely to be Foot and Mouth. Take some blood and a nasal swab and we'll send it off for testing. I'll see you back at the practice."

I hung up, glad for his reassurance that I hadn't made a complete fool of myself. My heart hammered with the nauseous sense of disaster averted. Unfortunately, as a new graduate I had come to understand it was my prerogative to make impossible jumps to not necessarily correct conclusions, but I would rather take the leap than be the one to allow a disease like that to get a foothold in the country once again.

Taking the requested samples, I gave the sterk a dose of a different antibiotic, anti-inflammatory, a diuretic as its lungs were distinctly crackly, and an off-license dose of a drug called planipart.

This medication contained a product called clenbuterol, licensed for use in parturition to relax the uterus, but was also a very effective bronchodilator. I thought this poor creature could use a good dose of something to expand its lung capacity. Leaving a very much more comforted Mr West to his stock I returned to the practice, to find Andrew waiting for me with the lab book open and ready.

"Are you ok, Gwen?" he asked with concern, passing me a mug of tea. "You had a bit of a scare."

"I feel like an idiot," I returned ruefully. I had spent the entire journey back considering my differential diagnoses, many of which were far more common and likely than FMD.

"We've all been there," he reassured me, drawing my attention to the lab book. "So now you've had a chance to think, what do you want to send these samples off for?"

Together we perused the selection of panels and picked the one that would give us the widest range of diagnostic tests. The samples were packaged and posted, and now I only had to wait for their return.

Five working days after my visit to Shieldhall Farm the test results came in. Unfortunately, the sterk in question was already dead, but that didn't lessen my curiosity as to what had been the cause.

Malignant Catarrhal Fever.

It was a condition I had briefly considered on the long drive back, along with a laundry list of other respiratory diseases, but had thought my other differentials were far more likely. MCF is caused by a virus transmitted from pregnant or recently lambed sheep or goats, although it can be several months between such contact and the onset of clinical disease, as had obviously happened in this case. The method of transmission to cattle is one of life's great unknowns, although thankfully the affected cow is what we call a dead-end host and will not transmit the virus to other animals. Affected cattle are often profoundly depressed with a very high fever. Complete appetite loss and severe corneal opacity causing blindness occurs. There is often crusting of the surface of the muzzle, mucosal ulceration and haemorrhage, as well as enlargement of all lymph nodes.

My patient had been something of a classical case, and I was glad of it. As a new graduate it was important to reinforce the old adage that 'common things are common', and not to jump to a conclusion before I had all the necessary information. It is unfortunately true that I, and most others newly unleashed up on the world of veterinary medicine, remembered and therefore suspected the unusual diseases because they were often more interesting and as such more easily memorable.

A lesson learned, and not easily forgotten.

CHAPTER THIRTEEN

October is for Snow…and more snow…

and more snow!

October began with a heavy snowfall of approximately four feet out of the blue overnight, turning the world into a bright white winter-wonderland. For me the awe and wonder lasted for all of about twenty minutes, at which point I opened my front door and discovered I would have to dig myself out if I wanted to get to my car, never mind anywhere else that day.

Thankfully I had been forewarned that winter hit hard in this part of the world, and when I'd seen snow shovels for sale in the local supermarket had made sure to buy one, even though seeing it among my purchases had given everyone a good laugh at my expense. Five minutes of concentrated shovelling later, I was hot, sweaty and even more grumpy than usual of a morning, but I had cleared enough of my garden path to escape captivity onto the slick, icy oasis of the pavement. Only to discover that if I wanted to get into work, I would have to dig my *car* out as well.

Living on a main bus-route sometimes had its benefits, the road itself was always rigorously kept free of snow and ice, but, unfortunately in this case, it wasn't the boon it had promised to be. When the snowploughs came through, all that snow had to go somewhere, and was consequently shoved to the side of the road, where everyone parked their cars, piling several feet of snow drift against the driver's side door, as I happened to have parked in that direction. I climbed into the car by the passenger door, earning some odd looks from my neighbours in the process as I contorted myself into an unusual shape to get over the handbrake and turned my Skoda on to de-ice the windows. Once I'd climbed back out on to the pavement, a seemingly more difficult prospect than getting *in,* I set about shovelling and scraping until I had a small avenue, wide enough to fit my car out, dug.

A disproportionate sense of triumph filled me. I felt as though I had already done a day's work, despite not being more than five meters from my front door and nearly twenty minutes late for my paid employment.

Turning off the traction control, as I had been warned it would just spin the wheels and dig myself in deeper, I carefully eased the car out of its confinement and onto the slushy road. I was grateful my commute was no longer than five minutes, but less than thankful the majority of the journey was down a hill that boasted a one in four incline. The disgusting, brown churned up snow made an uncomfortable crunching, squeaking sound under my tyres and I was reminded yet again of how much I really disliked the snow. After just about slithering to a stop at the small, but dismayingly busy roundabout at the end of the bypass, despite crawling along at barely fifteen miles an hour I spent the remainder of my white-knuckle journey in second gear and offering up prayers to any deity who might happen to be listening whenever I needed my brakes.

My arrival at work heralded yet another unpleasant surprise. Although the main road, and the hill behind the practice, had been gritted and kept clean that didn't necessarily mean our courtyard was similarly cared for. No; I had to dig myself into the practice as well.

I muttered and grumbled, my poor hands frozen solid despite the heat generated by my tasks, my bad mood getting more and more foul as the minutes ticked by. When I eventually stormed the snow-fortified back door of the practice, Leah, who drove an old Land

Rover Discovery and was therefore impervious to the hassles of the snow, like the rest of us mere mortals, greeted me with a cup of tea and a chocolate biscuit.

The girls really had taken to heart my boyfriend's advice that chocolate was the solution to all of my problems.

The snow remained stubbornly determined throughout October – and subsequently into the New Year – the only change being the volume falling each night, and whether I arrived home in time of an evening to reclaim my parking space. Or whether one of my sneaky, artful neighbours stole the conveniently cleared of snow spot for themselves.

A few days after the snow started falling, I drove out to the ironically named Sunnyside to microchip and draw a couple of horses for their passports. This in and of itself doesn't sound like a particularly taxing task, but it is fraught with more difficulties than is immediately obvious.

In this case, just getting to the yard proved difficult enough. Despite its four-wheel drive capacity the Skoda registered its objections to having to deal with the steep hill out of Lanchester, through Cornsay Colliery and into Tow Law. Snow on top of melted snow that had already frozen into ice did not a pleasant road surface make. Finally, I slithered my way onto the yard, just grateful the car stopped before it hit the wall in front of me, and paused to gather my thoughts and calm my pounding heart before getting out to face the client.

Armed with my all-important red and black pens and microchipping equipment I trudged my way along the partially cleared, slightly treacherous path as the owner of the two horses appeared around the side of the house. Ms Stepford-Smyth was a tallish woman of indeterminate age, wearing oft-washed, well-loved jodhpurs, complete with expensive boots and Barbour jacket. Her unnaturally blond hair was held back from her face by a furry headband that was several sizes too large to be called discrete.

"Are you the vet?" she asked in a clipped, cultured tone that definitely didn't originate from around these parts.

"That's me," I responded as jovially as possible while feeling completely scruffy beside her meticulously groomed person.

"Very well then," she sniffed, looking down her rather elongated nose at me, as though I didn't quite meet her standards of what a veterinary surgeon should be. "Lacey will bring the first horse out..." She turned and raised her voice until it became almost shrill and I manfully struggled to stifle my wince... "Lacey, dear! Bring Figaro out now!"

Lacey, it turned out, was Ms Stepford-Smyth's daughter, and a more miserably resigned creature I had yet to meet. As she brought a beautiful black yearling colt from the stable block around the corner, head held high and forefeet prancing, she grimaced at me with obvious apology. Evidently, she was used to the manner her mother treated the 'hired help' and didn't necessarily agree with it.

Figaro came to a halt in front of me with ears quivering and nostrils flaring. Unfortunately, he didn't stay stationary for very long. He shifted his weight and fidgeted, flicking ears and tail and mane in an attempt to communicate with his ardent admirers that he would much rather be running free in a field than restrained *here* for our pleasure.

I hid my heavy sigh. This was going to be difficult; I could just tell.

"We'll microchip him first," I informed the Stepford-Smyths in my best professional, no-nonsense tone. I didn't think it would make the senior of the pair respect me more, but I knew I had to try. "And then draw him. If you could just hold his head slightly lower that'd be great."

Obviously as Figaro was already a decent sixteen hands, his neck was unhelpfully out of reach unless I wanted to stand on a box, and with an animal as restless as this one I wanted my two feet firmly on the ground, braced to spring away should it be required. Lacey obligingly tugged his head and neck into a far more accessible position and I brought my microchip scanner slowly up to sweep over the top third of his neck to make sure he wasn't already chipped. I heard Ms Stepford-Smyth sniff again in disdain that I hadn't immediately taken her word for it, but as it would be *my* fault if I double-chipped the horse, I always made sure to check.

Unfortunately, Figaro thought the white, hand-held scanner was the most terrifying thing he had ever seen in his entire life. Nostrils flaring, he partially reared; throwing his head right back in an attempt to escape the killer white thingy! Snorting and stamping he backed away from the scary thing, dragging the hapless Lacey along with him, and I valiantly repressed the deep, resigned sigh.

Of course this is the way things were going to go.

Eventually, after ducking and diving, weaving and wobbling for what felt an eternity I managed a reasonable scan of the horse's neck, discovering, *quel surprise!* it wasn't chipped. Ms Stepford-Smyth emitted yet another sniff. Lacey looked at me and shrugged. I shrugged back. It seems we had formed a silent alliance to get this over with as quickly and as safely as possible, regardless of her mother's views of the matter.

By some miracle of dexterity, or laser guided microchip – or perhaps more likely Figaro had exhausted himself in his attempt to escape from the scanner – I managed to embed the microchip in his neck without too much bother. If he had been any other horse, I would have considered the dancing that had already ensued a lot of bother but going on his previous performance it was relatively brief.

For the most part it is standard place to microchip a horse in the mid-third of the nuchal ligament; this is the ligament attached to the back of the skull and the spines of the third and fourth spinal vertebrae that allows the horse to raise and lower its head with ease, on the left side of the neck. However, I have sometimes scanned horses and found a microchip on the right-hand side or not even in the neck at all but floating over the withers. Most of *those* horses were Irish in origin, where I guessed that anything goes. It is common knowledge that a microchip can migrate, with growth or if it is inserted only under the skin, but I doubted they could move to the opposite side of the neck.

Now I just had to draw the horse.

Generally, a horse passport consisted of a microchip number as well as an appropriately marked silhouette of the animal, plus a written description of its identifying features. This was the part of the process I disliked. If there were less than five distinguishing features on the silhouette it would be rejected by the passport issuer and have to be re-written, with much hassle and annoyance on both our and the owner's part. Not only was that a pain in the neck, the description had to be done in layman's terms, rather than anatomical correctness, which meant I had to remember the difference between the cannon or the pastern, a whorl and feather, a prophet's thumb and a flesh-mark. Not to mention the various names and descriptions of the different markings of the head. White patches had to be drawn in red, markings in black and a veritable myriad of different hatchings and shadings lurked in between.

I was thankful Figaro was entirely black. However, it did mean I had to find five whorls or feathers or any other distinguishing feature that meant the passport wouldn't be sent back to be done a second time. With a horse as jumpy as this one, it took rather longer than it needed to, and by the time we had finished my fingers and face were so numb with cold I wasn't sure they were still attached anymore.

Finally, Figaro was returned to his stable and I breathed a sigh of relief. The second horse; a young chestnut filly called Papillon, because of the butterfly shaped white blaze on her forehead, was a far calmer customer than her stablemate had been. She flicked an ear and an eye at the microchip scanner as I ran it over the warm, supple expanse of her neck, but merely shook out her mane and snorted at the interloper. Papillon passed the microchip test with flying colours and stood with remarkable stillness while I ran my hands over her to identify whorls and feathers and any other distinguishing features.

Drawing *her* took a quarter of the time it had taken for Figaro, and thankfully I wasn't treated to anymore of Ms Stepford-Smyth's pointed sniffs.

After I had said a distant farewell to the senior Ms Stepford-Smyth, and a rather more sincere one with the much put-upon Lacey, I took my paperwork and navigated the treacherous slopes back to the practice. I was very relieved to pull back into the safety of the courtyard, joyfully stealing the coveted parking space beneath the canopy, as Andrew was still out on his calls. I had managed to defrost my fingers sufficiently in the car's heaters so I could actually tell I had hands at the ends of my arms but was in dire need of a restorative cup of tea before I made any attempt to sort through my papers.

The Horse Passport Agency had recently launched an online portal to enable paperless processing of the passport applications, which was all well and good, and environmentally friendly, but it did necessitate a reliable and relatively decent broadband connection. Unfortunately, Oakbank existed in a bubble of cantankerous computer software and broadband speed slow enough to make glacial migration look swift. The veterinary software regularly crashed the entire network, and it was often an exhausting wrestle to get anything done over the internet during office hours.

Tea and chocolate was definitely a must have if I was going to try to get these passports sent off before the end of the day.

As I entered the practice, Nurse Gwen appeared from reception, her eyes wide as she mimed a zipping motion across her mouth, indicating she wanted me to not call out my usual greeting. A quick hand gesture back into the waiting room informed me there was a client in there, one she evidently didn't want to know I was back in the building.

"Yes, Mr Kowalcyzk," I heard Leah say with a hard done by sigh, and I instinctively ducked down below the windowsill, tucking myself in against the kennel closest to the wall, making as small a target as physically possible. "I'll let Gwen know as soon as she gets back. I'm sure she'll be pleased to know how well Dotty is doing."

I couldn't hear Mr Kowalcyzk's grumbled response, even though I strained my ears to catch what was being said.

"I'm not here," I whispered fiercely to Nurse Gwen. "Don't tell him I'm here."

If Mr Kowalcyzk realised I was present then I would never get away from him, and never get any of my paperwork done.

"Goodbye then, Mr Kowalcyzk," Leah's voice rose just before the front door was closed with a somewhat indignant thud. "Grumpy old sod…" she walked back into the kennels muttering, her irritated expression transforming into one of amusement as she saw me hiding in the corner below the window… "You've just missed your favourite client."

"Don't even joke!" I returned, exasperated by the older man, whom I suspected was just lonely, but who took up far too much of my limited time. I threw a grateful glance at the other Gwen. "Thanks for the warning. I've got a load of paperwork to go through, as well as prescriptions to get written, and I wouldn't have got any of it out of the way if you hadn't rescued me!"

So saying, I commandeered a chair and disappeared back into my consulting room, the addition of the seating turning it into an office, to plough my way through the horse passports, written prescriptions and insurance forms that were awaiting my attention. The three of us usually took turns to do the boring paperwork of our profession, based on whoever was in the practice at the time and unoccupied, and this time it was my turn. Carl was still wrangling a difficult cystotomy, Andrew was out on farm up to his ears in the middle of a TB test, and I was the only one with time on my hands.

I dropped into my chair, opened my sandwiches and pulled the computer a little closer toward me. This was going to be a tedious afternoon.

It seemed that October was going to be a month of tedious official documents and paperwork.

A week later we had a Labrador Retriever from one of the local breeders booked in for BVA Hip score x-rays. Hip dysplasia is a common inherited orthopaedic problem of dogs and a wide number of other mammals. Abnormal development of the structures that make up the hip joint leads to joint deformity. 'Dysplasia' means abnormal growth. The developmental changes appear first and later one or both hip joints may become mechanically defective. At this stage the joint may be painful and cause lameness. In extreme cases the dog may find movement very difficult and may suffer considerably.

The British Veterinary Association, BVA and the Kennel Club have run a Hip Dysplasia Scheme since 1975 to assess the degree of hip deformity of dogs using radiography. Assigning a 'score' to a dog's hips helps breeders to assess the likelihood of an animal passing on this developmental joint deformity to their offspring and will hopefully help to improve the general hip health of the assessed breeds by careful dam and sire selection.

Unfortunately, although I was all for the hip-scoring scheme to produce healthier puppies less likely to suffer from cripplingly painful arthritis at relatively young ages, the paperwork, and difficulty of obtaining BVA standard x-rays made it a very tedious task indeed.

The animals needed to be fully anaesthetised to ensure they were sufficiently relaxed so we could position their limbs for a decent x-ray. The pelvis itself needed to be perfectly square, perfectly straight on the x-ray plate, the knees rotated inward so the head of the femur sat appropriately within its socket.·

This accurate positioning could be extremely time-consuming, requiring a complicated procedure of duck-tape, sandbags as weights, ties and spirit-levels. For a relatively newly graduated vet it was a daunting procedure to attempt. Out came my sheaf of university radiography notes regarding the proper positioning for hip-score x-rays, helpfully provided by a very knowledgeable and very kind radiography nurse during rotations, to be studied with in-depth precision. For a relatively simple sounding task it took a vast deal of preparation, and, with our semi-automatic x-ray developer, far longer than it should have.

The Labrador in question was a stout, stumpy version of the breed, with enough sub-cutaneous blubber that it could have easily been mistaken for a seal, somewhat innocuously named Revolver. Even the fact that he was a friendly, amenable sort of dog couldn't make up for us having to heft his incredible bulk up onto the x-ray table.

"Do you think I can claim this dog contravenes my safe lifting of weight in the workplace guidance to get out of doing this?" I asked Jess, who was once again my companion in this endeavour. "Even half this dog is well over my 12.5kg limit."

She simply raised an eyebrow in response. I didn't think I'd get away with it, but it was worth a shot.

Anaesthetising the dog using intravenous anaesthetic through a catheter, we each gripped an end and hefted his bulk onto the table.

"Ha-way man, Revolver," Jess huffed as we just about managed to achieve our objective. "What have you been eating? I can't believe that this is considered *ideal show weight*. He's fat! That's all there is to it!"

Jess ought to know. She bred and showed, what Andrew called 'bog-brushes', but were Shelties to the rest of us. She also judged at a few shows and was regularly disgusted by the excessive size of many of the dogs involved. Just as with show ponies what the showing fraternity considered 'show-fit' the veterinary world classified as obese, or, in some cases morbidly obese. And yet try to tell a breeder or show-er that their prize animal was overweight and it was as though you were calling their parenting into question.

I would never understand that faction of the pet-owning public.

"He's a lump of lard!" I exclaimed as we began to position the dog, struggling with his great weight and overflowing excess padding. "I can't even feel where his hips are. We're just going to have to take it and see how it comes out. It *looks* straight, but who knows?"

We took the x-ray, and unsurprisingly it wasn't straight. So, we took another. And another. And another.

It took us nigh on three-quarters of an hour to get an x-ray we deemed acceptable enough to send to the BVA for assessment, and looking at the final position of the dog, I couldn't believe that the hips were *straight* on the plate. Revolver himself was tilted at an alarming angle, and upon a quick examination of the image I couldn't help but wince.

A good pair of hips had greater than fifty percent of the femoral head located within the hip-socket, with a nice even, rounded articular surface, no lumps or bumps of defects in the smooth lines of the cartilage. Revolver's hips were not good. He definitely had hip dysplasia, even to my non-expert eye, and I failed to see how he would be judged as anything but a failure.

"It doesn't look good," I informed the client as I discharged the dog later on that afternoon, receiving a disbelieving scowl for my troubles. "We had to put him in a very strange position to get an image they'd actually assess. I doubt he'll get the scores you want."

"Both his Sire and Dam are Show Champions," his owner retorted haughtily, obviously wondering whether I knew anything about pelvic anatomy *at all*. "They both have exceptionally low scores. Of course Revolver is going to have good hips."

I chose not to argue with them, keeping my opinion that they were wasting both time and money sending the x-rays to be scored to myself. Some breeders believed they knew more than the vet and were immediately affronted if said vet attempted to tell them something they didn't want to hear. So, I curtailed my protests, took their cheque and posted the x-rays off to be assessed, all the while knowing exactly what was going to happen when they came back.

Two weeks later when Andrew phoned the owner to tell them the bad news about Revolver's shockingly high hip-score results, a complaint was immediately lodged.

"That young vet said the x-rays weren't good enough!" the owner protested through the hatch at reception. I chose to hide behind the corner and listen as Andrew dealt with the irate breeder. "I don't know why you would send sub-standard x-rays for assessment, I demand you re-take them and resend them! Revolver's parents are Breed Champions; he couldn't possibly have bad hips!"

It just goes to show what people hear, and what people choose to *believe* are two utterly different things. I was now glad I'd shown both Andrew and Carl the wonky hips the day I'd taken them to confirm the x-rays were good enough to be sent off. Now Andrew could honestly offer his assessment of the images, and since he'd agreed with me that the hips were appalling, we were going to have one very unhappy client.

"Gwen showed Carl and I the x-rays," Andrew began in his most diplomatic tone. I had already learned a lot about dealing with awkward or angry members of the public by eavesdropping on his interviews with them, and I picked up more and more tips every day. "And we both agreed they were of diagnostic quality, but the hips were not particularly very good."

"But she said they weren't very good x-rays!" the client protested vociferously.

"They weren't very good hips," Andrew reiterated. "The BVA would never have assessed them if the x-rays weren't of the quality they are looking for. If they weren't diagnostic quality, they would have sent them back with a request that we retake the images before they could score them."

He paused, giving the client an opportunity to respond, but no words were forthcoming.

"I'm afraid genetics haven't been kind to Revolver," Andrew continued. "Just because his parents have good hips, it unfortunately doesn't mean that every single one of their offspring is going to be free from dysplasia."

"I want a second opinion!" the owner declared angrily. "I don't believe they could possibly be as bad as you say they are!"

I sensed the resigned sigh that Andrew wanted to release, although he did a very good job of holding it in.

"That, of course, is your prerogative," he said in a calm tone, but I knew him well enough by now to understand he was becoming irritated. "You are well within your rights to appeal their decision. You would have to contact the BVA to do so."

"That's what I'm going to do!"

A moment later the front door slammed with rather more force than necessary and I deflated against the wall, feeling a nagging sense of failure tugging at my stomach. Perhaps I *hadn't* taken a good enough x-ray. Perhaps if we had repositioned him a little, we might have improved the hip-score.

Doubt was a dark veil across my thoughts. Perhaps there was something else we could have done. I wasn't sure what it might have been, only that there must have been *something*.

Andrew appeared around the corner shaking his head with sharp annoyance.

"Idiot," he muttered pointedly, and then seeing the stricken expression on my face, hastily added. "Not *you*, Gwen. You took a perfectly good x-ray of utterly atrocious hips. The BVA made the right call. The owner's the idiot for thinking otherwise. Sometimes there's no talking sense into breeders. They live in their own little worlds."

"I know that," I returned in a tight voice. "But what if he starts to go around bad-mouthing the practice, saying we can't take proper x-rays?"

It wasn't an unwarranted fear. The breeding and showing community was a closely knit group, and sometimes more judgemental and suspicious than any other group of people I had ever come across.

Andrew shrugged with perfect unconcern.

"Let him," he retorted. "We don't survive on doing hip-scores, and most of the breeders who do use us are perfectly happy with our services. One discontented loud-mouth isn't going to change their minds."

I hoped so. Clara, who had been seated uncomfortably in reception while the breeder argued with Andrew came up and gave me a friendly, comforting shoulder bump.

"Don't let him get to you, Gwen," she advised pertly. "If you take to heart everything that unhappy clients say when they're in the wrong you'll spend most of your life completely mortaled."

Clara had obviously been watching a little too much *Geordie Shore*, where the main characters *got mortaled* – paralytically drunk – on a very regular basis. I hadn't understood the origin of the phrase until I had moved to this side of the world.

A thick skin, like a good poker-face was an essential commodity as a veterinary surgeon. I straightened my shoulders and forcefully shook off the doubts that plagued me because of this latest episode. Just as Andrew had said, if the x-ray hadn't been of good enough quality then the BVA wouldn't have bothered examining them.

I could take a decent x-ray. I *had* taken a decent x-ray and done my best for the client, even if he didn't appreciate it.

Clara grinned at the determination I felt not to let his words distress or disturb me.

"There you go, man," she bumped my shoulder a second time. "That's the Gwen we all know and love. Now off you trot. It's your turn to do paperwork again."

"I thought it was Andrew's turn?" I said slightly puzzled.

"Ahh," my employer tapped the side of his nose jokingly. "But I took care of that irate client for you. You can repay me by doing my paperwork!"

I gave an exaggerated groan, to which they both laughed, and dragged my feet and a chair along behind me as I went to once again transform my consulting room into an 'office'. I didn't really feel particularly put out by the good-natured demand. The light-hearted banter and serious innuendo that floated around the practice on a regular basis was all part and parcel of life as a veterinary surgeon. Perhaps it was an inappropriate, dark sense of humour that most vets possessed, but it was ours, and it was hard-won. Our bleak humour and less than PC jokes were borne out of blood, sweat, physical pain and tears. We worked damn hard for it. And if the outside world didn't properly understand it, then it was their problem.

One of the best parts of working in this environment was the craic and the camaraderie that insulated us from the harsh realities of our profession. Because if you didn't laugh, then you would cry. And if you were crying all the time, you wouldn't be a very effective vet.

CHAPTER FOURTEEN

November... You want me to use THOSE?

November was the month I was given my introduction to the serious task of dehorning and castrating bull-calves. And as with the majority of my experiences in the last eight months it was a case of take a deep breath, pull on my big-girl pants and do what had to be done. My bosses gave me guidance and the support when I needed it, but generally just let me get on with it.

Most efficient farms, dairy farms in particular, disbudded their calves either with a dehorning iron, or with caustic paste, in the first few days of life, and castrated the bulls in the first month. This practice ensured much less man-time and cost was incurred as opposed to the difficult, arduous, physical task of actually dehorning an animal with sizable horns, and bigger testicles that ran the risk of a serious bleed or infection. However, trying to communicate this change in management strategy to farmers who'd done what they were doing for the last fifty years – *if it was good enough for me fatha, then it's good enough for me!* – was another matter entirely. It usually meant we continued to do what we had always been doing, regardless of whether the change was one for the better.

For my first exposure to this particular management practice I was sent out to visit a Mr Whittaker at Mull Close. Mr Whittaker was a kindly, older gentleman who bred relatively well-behaved Limousin cattle – almost an oxymoron in regard to that particular breed! – and was somewhat hard of hearing, making communication outside in all weathers something of a challenge. However, despite the difficulties of making myself heard, his farm was an ideal place to learn the intricacies of this not difficult, or complicated, but necessary to master procedure. Not only were his animals well-handled, and therefore relatively bomb-proof – meaning that they wouldn't sooner kill you than look at you – his handling system was unusually good and efficient.

Cattle were moved from a pen at one end of the yard through a series of two-way gates to be separated out into smaller pens before they were pushed through a high-sided, single-file race into a crush with an automatic locking head-yoke. This meant individual animals could be isolated and treated with remarkably little danger to the life and limb of the operators, as opposed to some of the handling systems I had subsequently come across. Sometimes it was little more than a couple of hurdles held together with baler twine that wouldn't stand up if subjected to a stiff breeze, never mind a number of fractious, flighty animals.

The only unfortunate part of this situation was the cattle themselves. As quiet as they were, Mr Whittaker chose to keep his animals until they were at least nine months old before deciding to dehorn and castrate them. This meant the horns they possessed were at least five centimetres thick and required some considerable force to effectively remove them. And, as a consequence, a serious amount of blood spatter and other mess inevitably ensued.

Before I had set off for my morning's work I was going through my car making sure I had everything I needed; local anaesthetic, artery forceps to clamp off any awkward bleeders, catgut for a similar purpose and plenty of anti-inflammatory pain relief, Andrew unexpectedly joined me as I was half-in, half-out the boot, once again balanced precariously on the bumper. His expression was one of good-natured amusement, my height, or rather lack thereof, a constant source of entertainment for the entire practice team.

"You're going to need these," he was evidently referring to the, what I can only describe as garden shears on steroids, balanced on his shoulders. "I can guarantee you're not going to want to wire off twenty pairs of horns on your own. We usually use these big loppers for Mr Whittaker's cattle."

The 'big loppers' were one of the collection of antiquated, terrifying-looking equipment in the glass case on the x-ray-room wall I had assumed on my interview was a museum of sorts to the bad old days of veterinary medicine. They consisted of a rounded head with a cutting blade in the middle, concave on one side, controlled by the two and a half feet wooden handles that acted a little bit like a guillotine. I assumed that the convex surface of the head was placed against the skull with the horn in the middle of the two blades and to make a cut the handles were forced into the centre. I had no idea how Andrew expected me to close the handles with a large horn caught in between. I was strong for my size, but that was a bit much.

Andrew laughed at the nonplussed expression I was unable to keep from crossing my features. Without asking for my consent he deposited the 'big loppers' into the boot with the rest of my equipment.

"Trust me, you'll thank me for it when you see those beasts!"

I remained dubious, but nevertheless went on my way with those almost horrifying shears rattling around in the back of my car. I couldn't imagine any situation where I would want to use them, but Andrew knew our farm clients far better than I ever would, and he was generally always right.

Arriving at my destination, I pulled into a meticulously clean farmyard and parked on one side of a separating gate in front of the outbuildings. As I was gathering my equipment Mr Whittaker appeared from the house, dressed in a worn pair of overalls, with a flat cap covering his thinning hair. I, on the other hand, was wearing so many layers beneath my waterproofs that I resembled the Michelin Man. It was surprising I could actually lower my arms to my sides the amount of clothing I had on, but I was the sort of person who felt the cold exceedingly harshly, and if I was to function, I needed layers, a scarf and a hat. I'd like gloves as well, but that would unfortunately make actually doing my job somewhat difficult.

Hefting my equipment, although Mr Whittaker immediately commandeered the big loppers, I followed my companion across the slippery, icy expanse of the ridged concrete yard to the free-standing crush attached to the front of his fixed race, trying not to scowl at the open sky above it. I would have liked at least some form of canopy to shelter us from the elements, as the iron-grey sky was leaking a steady flurry of snowfall that was already sticking to my eyelashes, making it necessary to rapidly blink almost constantly to actually see where I was going. My work wellies were steel toe-capped, several years old and the soles were not particularly good at dealing with the treacherous conditions of the last couple of months. I was hoping that I didn't end up falling flat on my back during the course of the morning.

Once I was set up against the wall of the shed beside the crush for some form of shelter from the unending precipitation, with a bucket of warm water – luxury! – to wash my hands, Mr Whittaker took himself off to fetch the first batch of beasts for my attention.

They came out of the shed at speed. Obviously having been shut inside for several weeks since the turn of the weather these young beasts were full of verve and vigour, springing and kicking across the dangerously slick yard, making me wince at visions of broken bones and calls to the Fallen Stock company for an emergency slaughter.

Thankfully without any damage to life and limb the excitable cattle were corralled behind a complex series of gates and separated out into smaller more easily managed batches. There were forty-odd animals in this group, approximately half of them bull-calves requiring both castration and dehorning, while the heifers needed but one of the two procedures.

Mr Whittaker efficiently manoeuvred his cattle through his handling system, letting the roughly twenty heifers back out into the collecting yard, as castrating was the first task to be accomplished for the day. One by one the bulls were pushed through the race into the crush for my attention. Heads caught in the yoke and a kick-bar firmly in place for my safety I began the repetitive process of castrating the bulls. An injection of an anti-inflammatory painkiller under the skin, both for this procedure and the one to follow, precluded some local anaesthetic infiltrated into each spermatic cord of the individual testicle, giving it several moments to get to work. I used a chlorhexidine surgical skin preparation scrub to clean any mud or muck off the scrotum before making my incision. Under farm-yard conditions it was difficult to create an aseptic environment, but I was determined to try. Just because they were cattle and viewed as hardier than other species and not necessarily requiring such careful preparation, I was determined to stick as closely to best practice as possible.

There are several ways to castrate a bull and each farmer, vet and veterinary practice has their own preference. In very young animals, legal only in those less than twenty-four hours old, it is possible to encircle the neck of the scrotum with a rubber band that constricts the blood-flow to the testicles causing them to shrivel up and in short order wither away without any other veterinary intervention. This method is most popularly used in lambs, as castrating tups at an older stage of their lifecycle is rather more fraught with difficulty due to the much larger blood supply to the testicle. Some farmers prefer to use a burdizzo; a large clamp designed to break the blood supply to the testicles, once again causing them to wither away, while leaving the scrotum intact. Burdizzos, affectionately christened 'nippers' by the profession at large, unfortunately, on occasion, can be less than one hundred percent effective. Sometimes, despite having been 'nipped' at a young age some bull calves can still retain functioning testicles and cause severe disruption of the smooth running of a management system should they be kept penned up with young heifers.

This downside is why many farmers preferred to physically

castrate their animals. As they were often inclined to say; if they could see the testicles on the floor then they could be certain they wouldn't be able to do the job. Mr Whittaker was one of those farmers.

Grasping the scrotum at the neck I stood to one side, to reduce the chances of getting kicked, I gripped my scalpel blade tightly, swallowed the small niggle of nerves that bubbled up from my stomach, and made a long U-shaped incision through the skin and the tunica covering the testicle, until I had completely exposed the organ in question. Placing the scalpel securely out of the way I used my fingers to tear through the thin membrane attaching the epididymus to the body of the testicle. Separating the head of the epididymis from the testicle, I employed a variation of the 'twist and pull' method of castration, by twisting the two separated parts of the testicle around one another, while applying steady, firm pressure away from the animal, until both parts quickly pulled away from their anchors in the inguinal canal. Due to the torsion and tension applied by the 'twist and pull' of the procedure there was very little in the way of haemorrhage, making the whole method relatively atraumatic, despite its seemingly brutal appearance. A quick application of the farmers' favourite antibiotic blue-spray, and the beast was released to stand calmly with its fellows in the collecting yard.

Between each animal a few moments were spent observing the released beast, watching to ensure there was little to no bleeding from the surgical site in evidence. A slow drip was acceptable; as long as it was possible to count the drops we weren't particularly concerned. However, if the bleeding was a stream then we would have to get the animal back into the crush and root around for the troublesome vessel, as it was entirely possible for a beast to bleed to death due to a problematic castration.

Beast after beast entered and evacuated the crush, each one being given the same treatment, until all twenty-five bulls had been relieved of their bollocks and me and the crush were decorated with a mixture of scarlet and manure. My back was beginning to ache from the length of time I had spent bent over, my fingers frozen into the pose required to hold a scalpel blade, and I wasn't sure I was capable of moving them into a different shape. The snow was still falling in a light dusting of icing-sugar over the steaming backs of the animals clustered at one corner of the yard, regarding me with a deep sense of censure in their liquid brown eyes.

"Time for a cuppa, pet," Mr Whittaker said gruffly as we let the last of the now bullocks out. He raised an eyebrow as he surveyed my shivering, cold form and blue lips and fingers, while he seemed to barely feel the cold at all. "You look frozen, henny."

"I-it i-is a b-bit c-cold," I managed to stutter out through my numb lips, slowly fumbling with my equipment to ensure all hazardous materials and sharps were disposed of in a secure and safe manner. I couldn't feel my fingers, and when I did attempt to move them sharp needles of unpleasant sensation shot up and down my arms as though someone was stabbing razors all the way along my fingers. "I-I co-could do with a c-cuppa."

Feeling as though my limbs were not quite attached to the rest of my body, I stumbled ungainly on the icy concrete as I followed an astonishingly sure-footed Mr Whittaker toward the house, welcoming the warm heat of the utility room on my frost-burnt face. Then came the uncomfortable rush of sensation, the tingling, jaggedness of feeling returning to my numbed extremities that made me want to rub and rub at it until I scratched off that hideous sense of pins being driven into my cheeks and fingers.

Mrs Whittaker, a lovely grandmotherly woman who I had never seen without her flowery pink apron, or the smell of baking lingering around her, met us at the entrance to her spotlessly clean kitchen, tutting with sympathy at my frozen state.

"Look at you, pet," she clucked reprovingly, shaking her head as though she just didn't understand. "Chilled to the bone, you are! Being outside in all that weather!"

She pressed a steaming mug of tea into my hands, which still weren't working quite properly, meaning I almost dropped the mug as it burned my icy flesh. Momentarily I recoiled from the smarting sting, before hunching over the beverage and inhaling it as quickly as possible, regardless of the scorching discomfort of my mouth. I needed the heat far more than I cared about the pain.

"Aye," her husband chipped in. "T'is a bad day for it, but needs must, I s'pose. We're reet rattlin' through 'em though."

"It's a great system," I praised his handling facilities, knowing that on some establishments it would have required twice the time to get through half the animals. "It really makes life simpler when you've got a good race and crush to keep them under control. It's nice to not run the risk of being kicked in the face!"

"Here you go, pet," Mrs Whittaker disappeared momentarily into her kitchen, returning with a couple of absolutely massive slabs of cake. They wouldn't have looked out of place as doorstops, and I wondered whether I would be able to fit even part of a slice into my mouth. "Have some cake; you're such a tiny wee thing! Ya need a bita meat on ya bones to survive this weather."

I happily chose a slice of the offered cake, judging it and my tea as I consumed them both with enthusiasm. And then we had to go reluctantly back out into the filthy weather and wrestle with forty-odd cattle to dehorn.

Our first act was to run the whole bunch through the race and crush to inject local anaesthetic into the area halfway between the base of the ear and the corner of the eye. There is a bony ridge in this area where the appropriate nerve runs. In younger calves it is generally only necessary to block the cornual branch of the lachrymal nerve, but in older cattle the cornual cervical nerve also needs to be blocked. In this case I also applied a ring block around the circumference of each horn in an attempt to numb all innervation to the site in question. Each animal was marked with a number, one to ten as we had separated them into five batches, and then released to stand for a period of time to allow the anaesthetic to work its magic.

Then came the moment for the big loppers.

As the cattle were run into the crush for the second time, each one was further restrained by a halter secured to the bars of the crush to prevent any unwanted head movement at a critical time. As expected, I really didn't want to use the wire to remove any of these horns.

There are a number of different methods of removing horns from cattle. With large animals such as these it's either the big loppers or via the use of embryotomy wire. A long loop of wire is passed around the base of the horn, with handles attached to either end, providing something sturdy and atraumatic for the vet to get a good grip on. The wire is then moved in a sawing motion to cut through the tough tissue, the fiction of the movement, if done quickly enough, also cauterising the blood vessels supplying the horn. This procedure was the reason why I spent so much time on the rowing machines at the gym, but also provided me with yet another reason to bemoan my small, slight stature. The trick with wiring off horns is to lean back into the motion, providing extra bite of the wire into the tissue. So not only are most male vets a good deal stronger than I, but they are also generally heavier than me, meaning they have far more weight to put into the removal of horns.

As Andrew had predicted, I was immensely grateful for the presence of the big loppers. Even if I did consider them a bit barbaric.

Unfortunately, as *I* had predicted, once the horn was in the centre of the blade, there was absolutely no way, even with the best will in the world, I was going to be able to close them with enough force to cut through the sturdy, toughened tissue in question. Thankfully, despite being in his late sixties, Mr Whittaker was a wiry, brawny sort of man, who was – like many farmer and farm workers – much stronger than he looked, and I think it greatly pleased him to be able to do something requiring such tremendously physical man-power.

Each horn was cut with the sickening crunch of flesh and a sharp tug that had the required appendage dropping to the ground. Blood spurted in wide arcs from the skin vessels close to the skull, like any scalp wound bleeding profusely, disproportionate to the actual injury, and stubbornly refusing to cease. I was happy that Mr Whittaker had his own propane powered disbudding iron, which I employed as a rather effective cautery system for those troublesome bleeders. And because my nerve blocks were successful, neither of us was unceremoniously flung across the yard and the cattle barely felt a thing!

Dehorning took considerably longer than the castrating had, and by the time we had finished, the sky, which had never really achieved daylight status in the first place, was gradually beginning to darken. Upon consulting my watch after the last animal burst from captivity with bellow of displeasure, I saw it was nearly three o'clock, and my stomach sharply reminded me that I had missed lunch by a considerable length of time.

"Al-reet, pet," Mr Whittaker announced with a degree of satisfaction, a reflection of my own feelings at the successful completion of such a massive task, as we both stretched out our protesting spines and he helped me gather my bits and pieces. "That's the lot. A job well done, I'd say. C'mon, I'll tek ya to where ya can wash-up, henny."

Across the yard we went and into one of the outbuildings I had parked in front of, containing a startling number of engines and tractors in various stages of being dismantled that would have had my automotive engineer brother practically drooling. The lighting was poor, the lonely bulb swinging from the ceiling not doing its office in illuminating the gloom, as Mr Whittaker turned on a tap connected to a hose in the far wall. To my pleasant surprise the water was warm, and I was happy to partially defrost my frozen body as I squirted the thick, orange disinfectant called Fam, generally favoured by farm vets, onto my brush to get through the liberal coating of muck and blood on my waterproofs. Unfortunately, although Fam is a very effective disinfectant, it also had the terrible habit of eating through the vulcanised rubber of the waterproof protective clothing, making their turnover in a busy practice extremely rapid.

Clean, and almost able to feel all my body-parts, I piled all my gear back into my car, and drove back to the practice via the local supermarket to purchase a large volume of food for my lunch. I was vaguely bemused at the sidelong glances I received from the other shoppers and the frankly horrified expression of the cashier as she rapidly served me without quite managing to make eye-contact. That was until I happened to glance at myself in the rear-view mirror and realised I had spatters of claret all over my face. I had forgotten I had been sprayed with blood during the castrations and the dehorning, bodily fluids on my face a somewhat day to day occurrence of my everyday vetting life.

My arrival at the practice was greeted with the usual good-natured teasing.

"Did you get lost?" Carl enquired with a smirk, despite still being arm-deep in the midst of an operation, as I staggered in through the back door, burdened by my equipment in need of cleaning, barely able to feel my feet or my fingers.

"Tea," I grunted at him and the room in general, as I deposited my cargo with a loud clatter beside the sink.

Gwen laughed, but took pity on my miserable state and departed the prep-room, rapidly returning with a steaming mug that I practically snatched from her hands.

"Cold," I muttered through almost chattering teeth as I desperately hugged the hot drink to my chest, practically wrapping my body around it in an attempt to absorb some portion of its warmth. "So cold."

"How did it go?" Big-Gwen, as I was known as Little-Gwen, asked with some sympathy.

"Mr Whittaker had to use the big loppers," I returned ruefully. "But otherwise it didn't go too badly, although I frightened everyone at the shops."

I made an encompassing gesture at my blood-streaked war-mask and another laugh burst from her lips.

"Go wash," she pointed sternly at the sink before folding her arms in front of her. "You're not coming into the rest of the practice covered in that much muck. What happened to your inside shoes?"

The nurses had decreed the boots I wore on my farm visits, between getting out of the car and putting on my wellies, were banned from the main sections of the practice, because I generally ended up tracking mud and other things across their clean floors. This had necessitated the purchase of a pair of slip on crocs in which to consult, because I had already learned that keeping the nurses happy meant a much pleasanter environment for everyone involved.

"They're in the back kennel," I jerked a thumb toward the area where the freezer was concealed; the out of the way corner also containing our 'isolation' kennel that was mainly used as a storage facility for the vets' junk.

"You wash, I'll get them," she instructed, already disappearing around the corner to collect the required items of footwear. "Then we've got a busy afternoon surgery coming. You're going to have to eat on the fly, I'm afraid."

I groaned loud enough for her to hear, but ultimately did as I was told. Being a vet sometimes meant being rushed off my feet without much opportunity to catch my breath or take a seat to grab a bite to eat. It was a situation that everyone in this profession was intimately familiar with. Many of us complained about it, quite a few times it caused an uncomfortable bout of indigestion or the feeling of starvation when we didn't have the chance to eat at all, but collectively we just knuckled down and got on with it. The veterinary profession should have adopted the mantra *Keep Calm And Carry On* as our collective mission statement, because that's what we very regularly had to do. There was no room for someone to lose their head, to dither or panic when faced with an unexpected emergency or a lost opportunity to have a meal. Get on with it, do the job and stuff your face with chocolate when it's all over. That's what needed to be done.

There were sick and injured animals in need of attention.

CHAPTER FIFTEEN

December... A season of goodwill... Really?

Decmber was one of those strangely surreal months in the life of a veterinary surgeon. While everyone else began to anticipate the joys of the season and looked forward to groaning tables ladened with treats and goodies for excessive consumption, most vet practices made sure they had stock-piles of apomorphine and dreaded the inevitable pre-Christmas cull.

Although I had certainly *heard* of this phenomenon, I had always taken it all with a rather large pinch of salt, regarding the tall tales older vets told as something of an urban legend designed to unsettle us new grads. The profession had a long tradition of tormenting, not in a malicious way, those who came after us, and I had blithely assumed this was another of those things to be disproved by clinical practice.

But I was wrong. It was all true.

In the weeks leading up to Christmas we found the numbers of animals being euthanised almost tripled compared with any other time of the year. I no longer had any reason to wonder why we had put in an extra-large order for euthatal at the beginning of the month. Our only problem now being that we didn't necessarily have sufficient room to store all the dead animals awaiting collection by the local pet crematorium. People obviously didn't want to spend their Christmas holidays with their old, incontinent cat or dog, deciding that now would be a good time to act upon the hints, perhaps given months previously, that it was time for fluffy to go.

I know it might sound harsh of me, but the hard truth of the matter was that being constantly bombarded with euthanasia after euthanasia had the effect of inducing compassion fatigue in each one of the practice team. It wasn't that we didn't *care,* but it just wasn't feasible to grieve for every pet that died, just because there were so very many of them.

The only benefit it did have, if it could be considered a benefit at all, was to help *me* become inured to the procedure. Seeing it so often, performing the service so frequently enabled me to engender a professional clinical detachment. While I still sympathised greatly with the owners of each individual pet, I no longer felt like my heart was bleeding every single time.

How good, or bad, this development was for my mental health remained to be seen.

December was also a month of staff holidays, new locums and the beginning of the lambing season. Our current locum was a lady from New Zealand a few years older than me, called Kit. She operated at all times with that typical Australasian, laidback approach to life. Nothing seemed to bother or upset her quiet, easy equilibrium; not rotten calvings that ended in an embryotomy, giving her a horrific skin infection in the days following it, irate clients, or difficult, life-threatening surgeries at oh dark thirty when the vets in question had already had far too little sleep in the days leading up to it.

And for the latter, I would always be immensely grateful.

It happened one night on call in the middle of December. I was awakened from an uneasy sleep at one o'clock in the morning by the harsh, stomach churning notes of the Nokia ring tone. I had only got to bed an hour previously due to a bad calving that had thankfully missed becoming a caesar by the skin of my teeth. Fumbling blearily on the nightstand for the work phone, I resisted the almost overwhelming urge to throw it out of the window, my usual professional phone-voice not quite up to snuff at such an ungodly hour.

"Oakbank vets, emergency," even to myself my voice sounded weary and disorientated. I fell back onto my pillow, desperately struggling not to fall back asleep. Both on call and normal surgery hours had been incredibly busy lately, and I was exhausted.

"I think the dog's dying," the voice on the end of the line took me several moments to place, but finally recognition filtered through my grinding gears as I realised it belonged to the husband of one of our clients who ran an eventing stables. He was a sensible man who kept a flock of pedigree sheep and wasn't prone to over-excitability or exaggeration.

"What's happened?" immediately adrenaline shot through my body like a lightning bolt, snapping me into immediate wakefulness.

"Me and Sarah got back late from an event, and I fed Gunner before we shut everything up for the night. He went out into the back and didn't come back when I called him," Mr Brownlow was a somewhat stoic man, but I could almost touch the raw emotion in his voice. "I went out to look for him and he'd collapsed at the bottom of the garden. His belly is all swollen."

A red strobe warning light immediately screamed over the inside of my skull and I felt my stomach bottom out with sickening dread. It sounded very, very bad. Gunner was a pointer who had collapsed directly after consuming a meal, and I would assume had been running in the garden. One pre-emptive diagnosis, only one, ripped through my brain, bringing devastating panic along for the ride.

The dog had a GDV.

GDV or Gastric Dilation and Volvulus, is a condition seen most commonly in deep-chested breeds, often in association with being fed directly before or after exercise. The stomach can dilate, because of food and gas, and may get to a point where neither may be expelled. As the stomach begins to dilate and expand, the pressure in the stomach begins to increase, causing a potential disruption to the circulatory system. If the stomach becomes large enough it can rotate within the abdomen, cutting off the blood supply to the stomach and spleen, leading to an abrupt drop in blood pressure, shock and collapse.

This condition required immediate medical and surgical intervention if the animal had any chance at all of survival. And even then, the risk of complications were staggeringly high.

All of this information streamed through my mind in the time it took for me to suck in a couple of calming breaths. The last thing the client needed was for me to sound like I was panicking, which I was.

"Can you get him to the practice right away?" I was already out of bed and struggling into my clothes, the phone awkwardly balanced between my cheek and shoulder. "I'll meet you there."

A couple of words of agreement and I was disconnecting the call. I was still wrestling with my jumper as I clattered down the stairs, risking a broken neck in the process. Another phone call to the nurse who was on call with me that night, Jess for her sins, requesting her to get to the practice pronto and I was out my front door and launching myself into my car.

The short drive to the surgery was a foggy blur as I tried to tamp down my rising trepidation, desperately trying to recall what I had been taught to do in this situation so many months ago. This was one of the few, genuine veterinary emergencies and there was no time for me to look anything up in a book. Right now, I needed that knowledge at my fingertips, and I was silently afraid that my inexperience was going to cost this dog his life.

I slithered and slipped into the courtyard, far too fast for the icy road conditions, but I didn't have room in my head to think about that. My whole body shaking, I rushed from one end of the practice to the other trying to gather all the equipment I would need. The oxygen and anaesthetic machine was the first thing to go on, then the x-ray machine. I was frantically digging out laporotomy kits and sterile gloves when Jess arrived on the scene.

Immediately her calm, no-nonsense demeanour helped to add a hint of calm to my looming hysteria. She took over preparations for the imminent surgery and packed me back into the office to await the arrival of our patient. I sat in the chair with jangling nerves and jiggling feet until minutes later the front door burst open.

Gunner arrived limp and losing the battle with consciousness in his master's arms. I hurried them into a consulting room and we lowered the critical dog onto the table. My clinical exam was quick and concise, although not from any conscious effort on my part. Astonishingly, rigorous veterinary training and muscle memory from all those nights spent in the ICU at university took over. Inwardly I was working myself into a nice, hysterical dither, but outwardly I was the picture of calm, collected professionalism. A little like a Swan; serene on the surface but paddling frantically underneath where no-one else could see.

Gunner's membranes were turning a worrying shade of pale blue, his heart rate far too slow. His abdomen was grossly distended and made a very distinctive 'pinging' sound, like flicking a beach ball, when percussed. There was absolutely no doubt in my mind what was the problem. Either we operated or we put him to sleep. There was no in between.

"Do it," Kev Brownlow instructed immediately. "Whatever it takes, just fix him."

He might be a farmer, used to life and death, but he loved his dogs. Sarah gripped his hand hard and squeezed to give him comfort. I had become good friends with them both over the last few months and I knew how difficult this was for them.

"There's no guarantee he'll pull through," I warned them gently, even as I efficiently went through the procedure of signing consent forms and preparing the dog for transfer to theatre where we could begin to pre-oxygenate him prior to anaesthesia. "Unfortunately, the risk of complications is high, but we'll do everything we can to get him through this."

Jess helped me carry Gunner through to theatre after the Brownlows departed. Placing an oxygen mask over his muzzle we quickly clipped and prepped his forelimb before crossing my fingers and praying for good luck at hitting the vein in this extremely compromised patient. For the longest moment of my life I thought I had missed, no flashback of blood immediately appearing in the catheter.

"Damn," it was the politest word to come out of my mouth in the last several minutes. My anxious gaze met Jess' concerned expression and I once again felt myself spiralling into a pit of doubt. "I haven't got this. I can't even see where I'm supposed to be aiming for. I'll have to redirect and try again."

"Wait!" Jess' exclamation stopped me before I could begin to reposition. "There, look, he's just got rubbish blood pressure."

To my amazement there was blood dripping into the hub, slow enough to make a snail look speedy, but there nevertheless. With no owners around there was no need to hide my triumphant fist-pump, or the high-five we exchanged once we'd got him connected to a bag of fluid at a very high drip rate. Anaesthetic given, we got an ET tube into his airway, meaning we could maintain the level of anaesthesia and also breathe for him if necessary.

The second order of business was to attempt to pass a stomach tube, which unsurprisingly wouldn't advance into the stomach. In all likelihood this was a torsion, but just to be completely certain of the diagnosis before we embarked on difficult and risky surgery, we carried him over to the x-ray room to get an image of his abdomen. I wasn't surprised to see a hugely distended gas and food filled stomach that was pushing all the rest of his organs out of the way. A quick glance showed the tail of the spleen in the wrong quadrant of the abdomen, confirming my suspicions. In an attempt to let some of that pressure off I inserted a needle into the greatest curvature of his grossly distorted abdomen, listening with some satisfaction when gas audibly hissed out of the puncture and his belly began to deflate by minute degrees.

"How's he doing?" I asked Jess through clenched teeth as I watched her remove the stethoscope from her ears, a serious, worried expression on her features.

"Not good," she shook her head. "Heart rate forty, resp rate forty, his colour's poor. I'm not sure he's going to make it."

"We need to get him open right away," I responded, my voice wavering over the words. Surely someone far more capable than I should be responsible for this situation; but there was only me.

We quickly carried him back across the courtyard into the operating theatre and Jess began the process of preparing Gunner for the forthcoming procedure as I fetched *Fossum*, the small animal surgical bible from the small library of such books the practice kept. This book had illustrated step-by-step instructions on how to perform the surgery I was about to attempt, and since I had never even seen one in real-life before, I knew I was going to need it. *Fossum* was a veritable doorstep of a tomb, and I had to try three times before I could successfully pick it up, my hands were shaking so badly with anxiety. This wasn't a caesarean on a cow, or a relatively routine bitch spay. This was major, life-saving surgery on an already compromised animal and I was utterly terrified.

As I was scrubbing my hands there was a knock on the back door. Jess left her post at Gunner's side to quickly open it, before rushing back to maintain a constant monitoring of the struggling patient's vital signs. Kit's sleep-rumbled face poked around the edge of the doorframe, her blond hair in complete disarray as she rubbed her tired eyes. It was now nearly two o'clock in the morning.

"I heard the commotion," she supplied as she closed the door behind her. "What's happening, do you need a hand?"

It was evident we were dealing with a critical patient; otherwise we wouldn't be preparing to operate at such an ungodly hour of the morning.

"Have you ever done a GDV before?" I queried hopefully. Kit had been graduated for several years longer than me and despite having mainly worked with large animals I was anticipating she would have *some* helpful experience in this situation.

"No, never," her expression turned pale as she glanced at the dog on the table awaiting my attention. I snapped on the second of my sterile gloves as we were speaking and moved toward theatre. "Do you want me to scrub in and give you a hand?"

"Maybe, or maybe you could pass the stomach tube once I've corrected the torsion?" I returned. "He's pretty critical and I'd rather Jess just concentrated on the anaesthetic."

"Right then," she regained some of her colour and her habitual calm demeanour. "Show me the stomach tube, maestro and let's get this party started!"

I made my incision practically all the way from sternum to his lower abdomen and immediately his stomach tried to burst out to great me. The tissue was red and angry, but still looked viable enough, although there was always some worry with this procedure that the gastric blood supply had been constricted to such a degree that the stomach would begin to die, regardless of how successful the surgery might be.

The stomach was still very distended, despite our efforts to decompress it pre-surgery, and thick with food matter. I had really hoped I wouldn't have to decompress the stomach during the procedure, but I could see we would never be able to correct the torsion without doing something to reduce its massive bulk.

"Can I have a kidney dish please?" I requested, my voice trembling with nerves and I was astonished that my hands weren't likewise shaking. "I'm going to have to make a stab incision into the stomach."

Kit presented me with the appropriate dish, standing on the other side of the dog and making sure to maintain as sterile field as possible. Exteriorising a portion of the bloated organ I made a small incision with the scalpel, holding it over the dish to keep the abdomen as uncontaminated as I could manage under the conditions. A small amount of gas and gastric juice escaped, but there was little reduction in size of the stomach. It was still too large to rotate back.

I was going to have to enlarge my incision and physically remove the stomach contents. Just what I didn't want to do.

Putting on a second pair of sterile gloves, so I could remove them intraoperatively should they become contaminated, I exteriorised a larger portion of the curvature of the stomach, making sure to avoid the blood vessels and nerves innervating the viscous as I continued my incision until it was large enough to admit the practice's special gastric decompression spoon. This piece of equipment was actually a large dessert spoon, which Andrew had once in desperation had to utilise for a similar procedure several years previously and had ever since kept appropriately sterilised so no one would ever be in such a predicament again.

It was a tedious, nerve-racking procedure. I had to carefully spoon the semi-digested stomach contents into the kidney dish, maintaining my hold on the stomach itself so it didn't slip back into the abdomen, utterly compromising it with gastric acid, all the while knowing that the longer we took to complete this task the greater the risk of the patient not surviving the intervention.

I could feel sweat beading on my forehead and upper lip, slicking my spine between my shoulder blades until my tee shirt stuck uncomfortably to my skin. Neither of my companions seemed to be feeling any better. Kit's habitual banter was no longer in evidence and Jess' expression was one of deep worry as she continuously monitored Gunner's heart, breathing and colour. The drip was still rapidly running into his veins, the intermittent bip-bip of the pulse oximeter jangling my already rattled nerves. But at least I could take comfort in its steady rhythm. As long as it wasn't blaring out an alarm my patient was relatively stable.

Small mercies and all that.

Finally, as my back was beginning to cramp and my fingers felt that they no longer wanted to grip the spoon, I thought I had got as much of the mush out of the stomach as I could feasibly manage. It wasn't just dog food. Gunner had evidently got into the sheep pellets, the consumption of which, and subsequent swelling within his stomach, likely the cause of his current predicament.

Stitching the stomach closed seemed to take a lifetime, and I managed to somehow get into a muddle with my instruments and suture material several times. It was my anxiety and tiredness coming through, and I struggled to focus my exhausted gaze on my task as the hands of the clock crept closer to three o'clock.

"He's stable enough, Gwen," Jess said encouragingly as she evidently saw me beginning to falter. Unfortunately, at this hour of the morning my body had the less than useful habit of starting to shut down, regardless of what I was trying to achieve. "You're doing great. Just keep going."

The stomach was rotated in a clockwise direction, and after several heart-pounding moments of struggling with the awkward viscera, and violent cursing, I eventually saw success as it returned in a rush to its normal orientation. At this point *Fossum* directed the surgeon to inspect the stomach and spleen, which had been carried along with the volvulus, for damage or viability. I was immensely grateful that the spleen didn't look too worse for wear, despite the length of time it had been trapped by the torsion. I was relieved I didn't have to remove the spleen *as well* as correct the initial catastrophe.

At this point of the procedure I was supposed to perform a gastropexy – suturing a portion of the stomach to the body wall in an attempt to prevent it from being able to twist a second time. The description of the preferred 'belt-loop' method, involving dissecting between the layers of the abdominal muscles just behind the last rib and passing a loop of tissue between them made me feel almost physically sick. I wasn't certain I'd be able to achieve it without doing even more damage. It looked far too complex for my three-a.m. brain to manage to put together.

I looked between Kit and Jess with mounting panic. What was I going to do? I had to do something!

"I'd do it like a DA in a cow," Kit offered, evidently seeing I was about dissolve into hysterics.

I'd seen, and participated in, enough displaced abomasum operations in cattle to feel vaguely confident that I could comfortably replicate it in this procedure. Taking several deep breaths, I made a short incision through the surface layer of the stomach and the body wall, suturing them together, until I was satisfied it would hold.

Closing my mammoth incision seemed to take forever and a day, and by the time I had placed the last suture in the skin I was exhausted and physically broken in a manner I had only ever before associated with hard, physical exertion. I stripped off my gloves and stumbled out of theatre. Propping myself up against the wall, I felt my knees give way and slid in a barely controlled motion down until I came to an abrupt stop on the floor.

I wasn't certain I'd get back up again without assistance.

And we had still to recover Gunner from his anaesthetic. There was a chance that we had gone through all that effort and strain for the dog to simply not wake up.

We kept the ET tube, providing oxygen, in his throat until the very last moment. His colour had vastly improved since we had corrected the volvulus, and the moment I heard him cough in irritation at the tube I thought I was going to cry.

Ten minutes later we had him installed in a kennel, covered in blankets and surrounded by hot-hands – non-sterile gloves filled with hot water – as he began to raise his head and look around blearily, tongue hanging from his mouth at an awkward angle. A low, keening whine broke from his muzzle as he flopped back down, obviously disorientated and discomforted by his operation.

"Gunner, man, you idiot!" Jess muttered with a relieved exhalation of breath. She stroked gentle hands over the bemused dog's head and neck, helping to keep him calm and settled as he came around from the anaesthetic. "Why did you go and eat sheep food, ay?"

I was immediately on the phone to the Brownlows. I knew, despite the fact it was close to five o'clock in the morning, neither Kev nor Sarah would mind the disturbance; in fact, I would have been surprised if they had managed to get any more sleep than we had.

"Hello?" Kev's voice was taut with worry when he answered the call, obviously the only person ringing him at this ungodly hour would be the vets. "Is he alright?"

"He's awake," I immediately reassured him. "He's doing really well. We've corrected the problem, and so far everything's looking good."

I heard the breath explode out of him with relief. It might have been mixed with the beginnings of a sob that he struggled to suppress.

That was something I had never understood; why men felt they had to suppress, or even apologise to *me* for any tears they might shed, be it in relief, or grief for their pet. As far as I was concerned, this animal was a part of their life, their family, their heart. Far from condemning them for the expression of their emotions, I thought it was a perfectly reasonable, perfectly healthy response to the situation.

"He's okay," I heard him murmur away from the phone, and then his voice became clearer once again. "When can we come see him? When can we bring him home?"

"We'll want to keep him for at least a day," I informed them. "We have to make sure he didn't suffer a relapse, or any other complication from the surgery, and was eating before we thought about sending him home. If you come into the practice at about ten o'clock we'll have finished with morning surgery and you can spend a bit of time with him."

"Thanks, Gwen," Kev choked. "We're so grateful to you."

Ten days later on Christmas Eve, Gunner returned to the practice for his final post-op check and to have his sutures removed.

His entrance could not have been more different than the one he had made that night. Instead of being carried in, Gunner practically dragged Kev through the front door, tongue lolling and his sturdy, lean body bristling with barely contained energy. As I called him into my consulting room, he greeted me with his front paws on my shoulders and an enthusiastic tongue swipe across my face. Ugh!

"Give over y'great soft lump," Kev commanded with gruff affection as he pulled the dog back onto all four feet. The broad grin on his face belied his attempt to sound stern. "As you can see, the idiot is back to complete normality now!"

I laughed, happy that the surgery had been such a success. There were moments during the operation when I had been certain it was going to go the other way.

"I'm glad to hear it! Now, shall be try getting those stitches out?"

It took a good deal of scrabbling around on the floor, and several more licks before I managed to remove each one of the skin sutures I had placed early that morning ten days previously. The wound was healing perfectly, and I was glad to see they had been able to keep the dog from bothering it. In the future, all Gunner would have to show for his brush with mortality was a thin white scar upon his midline.

Their departure left me with lightness in my heart and a surge of triumphant adrenaline through my body. As miserable as parts of this month had been, it was the little, and not so little, successes like Gunner that made everything so utterly worthwhile.

On call might be exhausting. I might get kicked and bruised and battered by cattle and sheep and horses, but that dog, and the life I had saved, was exactly why I bothered to do this. Why any of us bothered to do this.

"You did good, Kiddo," later on that afternoon, in the pub across the road where the whole practice team had gone to celebrate the closing of the practice for Christmas, Jess slung an arm around my neck and squeezed. Her eyes danced with mischief. "C'mon, it's your round! Let's get the drinks in!"

CHAPTER SIXTEEN

January chaos

In small animal practice the month of January was generally a quiet one, a chance to get on with some paperwork and organise for the coming year. Many vets had christened it the post-Christmas lull, where pet owners, like the rest of us, were desperately wishing for payday after the expensive excesses of the Christmas period.

This 'lull' gave me the time to collect my thoughts about the year we had just left behind, and in doing so finally complete my blasted *PDP* – *Professional Development Phase* – sending it away for its tedious final review. I had done more vaccinations, cat spays and caesareans than I really wanted to count, along with all manner of other surgical and medical procedures, all of them dutifully logged in the appropriate places and emailed to my post-graduate Dean with the hope that soon I wouldn't have to think about it ever again.

She sent it back.

She wanted more reflection and self-assessment from me, on how I had grown and learned as a practitioner. What I would have done differently in hindsight and the things I regretted about my first year in practice. And most of all what I thought of the *PDP* process as a whole. I wanted to scream with irritation.

I didn't have *time* to spend two or three hours a night ruminating and reflecting on what I had done or achieved during the day. Not if I wanted to accomplish other, more important tasks, such as eating or sleeping. And neither did any of the other new grads in the same position as me. The vast majority of anyone I had ever spoken to about the *PDP* scheme thought it was a load of bollocks, a waste of precious time and space in my already overcrowded brain. We were busy people with busy on-call schedules, and there just weren't enough hours in the day to spend energy on something that was little more than a useless paperwork exercise.

I was tempted to let the Royal College know exactly what I thought about the process and subsequently had to keep my fingers away from the keyboard until I had overcome the urge. Instead I spent an hour adding blatantly sarcastic and facetious comments to my work, complaining about sheep caesars being hard on my knees and such like, in an attempt to communicate my displeasure. I thought perhaps someone would read it and realise how much everyone who had to do this pointless paper-pushing actually hated it.

My post-graduate Dean thought I lived a varied and interesting life, the deep, biting, scathing sarcasm flying directly over her head. Well at least she passed me this time, even if my comments hadn't been taken in the full spirit of how they were written.

However, regardless of how quiet things were on the small animal side of the business, the same could not be said for our farm calls. There we were as busy, if not busier, than we would be during the peak of lambing season. Livestock had needed to be housed much earlier than planned due to the dreadful weather conditions, which in general led to an increase in the usual problems associated with large numbers of animals sharing the same airspace for prolonged periods of time. Pneumonia was rife, as well as the metabolic diseases that normally went perfectly hand in hand with stress, competition for resources such as food and water, and late pregnancy. There wasn't a day that went by we weren't called out to an ewe with pregnancy toxaemia, or, as the season progressed a cow that had prolapsed her uterus after calving.

A prolapsed uterus was a somewhat daunting task to be faced

with. Obviously, a cow's uterus has to be large enough at birth to contain the calf, some of which are bigger than I am, so just imagine the size and weight of the flesh that is expelled in this instance. It's something of a challenge to wrestle with about three feet of organ at about fifty kilos a pop, especially when neither the uterus, nor the cow is particularly inclined for it to go back inside. If you were really lucky, the beast was an angry Limousin heifer who just wanted to try to kill you, as you tried to shove her uterus back through a passage that it didn't seemed to fit.

Generally, much swearing ensues, and for the most part I look as though I've just murdered someone after having completed such a task, requiring a complete change of clothes and a thorough wash. This was the call I had just returned from at about eight o'clock one snowy January evening on call, having taken the quickest shower known to man, soaking my blood and gore covered clothes in a bucket of cold water and washing up liquid – the best thing I've found for getting blood off fabric – while I inhaled a microwave ready meal, when the phone erupted yet again into life. I scowled at it, wondering whether Andrew and Carl would really be *that* bothered if I jumped up and down on it until it was as flat as a pancake.

I decided, with a reluctant wince, that they probably would.

"We've got a lambing," I recognised Kev Brownlow's voice and was immensely glad it wasn't his dog this time. If I never had to do another GDV again for the rest of my career I would be a very happy vet. Even nearly a month later I was still traumatised by the thought of it. "I think it's going to be a caesar."

Kev bred pedigree Beltex sheep, which is why he started lambing so soon into the new year and caused the practice no end of problems with the breed's issues. As a whole, Beltex lambs were very large and their mother's pelvic canals were not necessarily wide enough to allow them to pass without some form of intervention. Or, as Andrew was wont to say; the ewes were just too posh to push.

"Alright," I scarfed down the last remnants of my dinner and patted Mischief apologetically on the head. I was about to disrupt her usual evening occupation of stretching out on my knee and falling asleep, and the stripy little feline produced an indignant miaow. "I'll be there in ten minutes. I'd like warm water please!"

Taking care on the icy, treacherous roads, I nevertheless made good time getting to my destination, which was really just a short hop away from my house. Kev opened the gate to the yard so I could pull in off the road, protecting the Skoda from potential damage due to other drivers and the hideous weather conditions, and I followed him across the slippery expanse of concrete, the bitter, dank wind seemingly clawing grooves in my cheeks, into the relative warmth and shelter of the lambing shed.

The ewe in question was already penned up away from her fellows, and weighed twice as much as me, so I gladly allowed Kev to wrestle her to the ground in preparation for my examination. I had always thought of Beltex as particularly ugly creatures. Their squat, solid bodies were thick bones sheathed in slabs of double muscle and tight fleece. They had squashed, troll-like faces and a deep, rattling vocalisation quite unlike any other sheep breed I had ever come across. Just the size of them put me off the breed completely.

A liberal application of lube later and I was encountering the absolutely massive feet of the lamb that was the root of our problems. I didn't even bother trying to give it a pull. Those humongous feet crossed almost as soon as they engaged in the pelvic canal, and I knew if I applied any degree of traction then I ran the very real risk of killing the lamb and potentially damaging the mother as well. This particular ewe's pelvis was actually – shockingly – quite normal for a Beltex, her cervix fully dilated, but there was no way that lamb was coming out the back door. Not unless the physical laws of the universe momentarily decided to look the other way.

"It's definitely a caesar," I confirmed with a falsely put-upon sigh, propping my hands on my hips and giving him a mock glower. We had been here several times before. "Right then, you know the drill."

"I'll just get comfortable here," Kev retorted, doing as he suggested and settling more comfortably into the straw as he positioned the ewe on her right-hand side, giving me access to her left flank. "While you do your thing."

I had done enough sheep caesars at this point to have long ago lost whatever nerves I'd had on that first stressful operation. They were becoming something of a routine procedure, and I was almost certain I could do it in my sleep.

I clipped and scrubbed, cut and guddled around in her insides until I could yank the gigantic lamb from her abdomen. Clip to getting the lamb out took less than twenty minutes, and we chatted companionably about how the sheep, the horses and the dogs were getting along. I was glad to hear confirmation that Gunner was doing well, and seemingly hadn't looked back after his operation.

As we talked the lamb bleated and shook itself, splattering gore and uterine juices over both of us. As it staggered unsteadily to its feet, stumbling through the deep bed of straw like Bambi on ice, the monstrous baby decided the most likely place to get milk was from the back of my knee. It's quite difficult to concentrate on suturing when there's a lamb sucking on and intermittently butting your leg.

I was just about to start my skin sutures when Kev began to laugh.

"I think I have another for you to look at when you're finished," he chuckled, indicating with a jerk of his head a second ewe on her side a little ways away, a truly massive pair of feet protruding from her vulva. I couldn't suppress a soft growl at the thought.

One final suture, a liberal squirt of the farmer's best friend the blue spray, some jabs of antibiotics and pain relief, and the first ewe was good to go. We caught the second labouring ewe without too much difficulty – at least Kev made it look fairly easy – and a brief rummage around produced the same results as with the first. Thankfully our caesar box contained two complete surgical kits, so there was no issue with performing back to back operations, except perhaps for my knees and spine.

I was most certainly not laughing when, as I was finishing up the second caesarean, Kev spotted a third ewe in need of my attention. I threw a handful of gloopy straw at the dratted man as he continued to chuckle at the dark scowl upon my features.

"This is what you get for breeding pedigree Beltex!" I growled after checking our third lambing of the night and finding that it also was not going to pass the lamb by natural means. "Right, I'm going to have to boil a kit. She'll have to hold for half an hour."

We traipsed into the kitchen, shucking our filthy boots and waterproofs at the door and finding a large enough pan to fit my instruments into, setting it to boiling with a liberal splash of vinegar for twenty minutes. Thankfully it gave us the opportunity to have a cup of tea, a couple of chocolate biscuits and to thaw out our frozen limbs while we waited. When we first entered the kitchen, I could barely feel my poor beleaguered feet, but when we began to think about leaving I could just about discern I had appendages on the ends of my legs once again.

Why I thought a life as a farm vet was a good idea for someone with as poor circulation as I had is completely beyond me, but I couldn't imagine doing anything else.

When time was up, we carefully collected the boiling hot kit, taking care not to burn our hands on the scorching metal and returned to the lambing shed to complete the third caesar of the night. Kev caught the ewe, this one was showed a little more of the breeds habitual sass, kicking and struggling throughout the procedure, but we got a live lamb out of her, so thankfully the evening could be considered a success. Three out of three wasn't bad.

As I was washing up for the final time after the ewe had been released, I half-heartedly scowled at our client. To be honest I didn't have the energy, or the heart to do much in the way of teasing at this hour of the night.

"Don't take this the wrong way, Kev, but I really don't want to see you, or your sheep again tonight."

He merely laughed and helped me carry my stuff back to the car. Instead of going straight back home for another shower and to fall into bed, I went to the practice to clean and sterilise my kits in the hope that if I did so I wouldn't get called out again. The harsh gods of on call would hopefully take pity upon me if I was all prepared, and ensure the phone stayed mercifully silent. Fingers and toes all crossed. I really did need to get some sleep tonight if I was going to be at all functional the following day.

For a collection of scientifically minded, logically orientated people, vets in general entertained a shocking number of superstitions. Such as the belief that saying the dreaded 'q' word – quiet – in reference to a night on call would immediately damn you to suffering a busy and difficult night. Just like my certainty that if I didn't clean my kits it would therefore follow that I would have another caesarean to perform. It was a completely illogical supposition, but I have not yet been able to break myself of the superstition.

It was getting on for midnight when I finally managed to fall into bed for, hopefully the rest of the night of uninterrupted sleep. I was exhausted and aching from the length of time I had been kneeling on the floor of the lambing shed. If I didn't see another sheep for at least twenty-four hours I would be quite satisfied.

I couldn't have been in bed for more than fifteen minutes when the stomach-turning tones of the on-call phone ripped through the quiet of my bedroom once again. I recognised that number with a sinking sensation inside my chest and the noise that came out of my throat far more resembled a snarl than actual speech.

"You need to shoot that bloody tup," I muttered in annoyance by way of a greeting. I wouldn't have spoken to some of our farmers like that, but Kev and I had learned we had a very similar sense of humour, almost a meeting of minds, and we always had great craic regardless of what disastrous circumstances we were having to deal with.

"We've got another one," Kev laughed, completely unfazed by my bad-tempered words. He knew I didn't necessarily mean it.

"Right," I heaved a put-upon sigh, flinging off the covers with a deeply displeased huff. "I'll be there in ten minutes."

I suddenly had a most disconcerting sense of deja vu. Climbing out of bed I pulled on my clothes and once again made my way carefully to the yard. Kev was waiting for me to open the gate with a small grin on his face, helpfully collecting my gear from the boot and leading the way back up the familiar path to the lambing shed. Now that the night had drawn in the temperature had dropped even further, the snow was still falling, and I began to shiver despite the sheer number of layers swathing my frame.

"I really hope you aren't thinking of making a habit out of this," I said after I'd checked the fourth sheep of the night and found the lamb was also an utter monster.

"Bloody expensive habit if it is," Kev muttered, shifting position as he settled in for the next half an hour or so.

"I'm serious about shooting that tup," I retorted as I got on with clipping and scrubbing. "I hope we don't have to take them all out through the side door, because I'm going to get really annoyed if I have to spend all my evenings in this lambing shed. How many are you lambing this year?"

"Hundred and twenty Beltex and another coupla hundred mules," he replied.

"I'm going on holiday," I returned determinedly, frowning as I attempted to thread my needle despite the fact my hands were shaking with the cold. "Until you're done with the Belties at least. My back can't cope with this every day."

Thankfully the operation went as smoothly as possible in a non-sterile farmyard environment, and shortly we were rewarded with the happy bleating of yet another massive lamb as it sucked its mother. I stretched out my poor, abused shoulders, neck and spine, really wishing there was someone available to crack my various joints and vertebrae back into some form of alignment. I felt crippled, as though I would never be able to stand up straight ever again. What I really wanted was a nice long soak in a scalding hot bath, but it was now pushing on two in the morning and I needed sleep far more than I needed a bath.

Getting home, I did a quick, cursory clean up, not really wanting to drag sheep shed between my sheets, before struggling into my pyjamas and falling face first into bed, hoping for a peaceful rest of the night. I hadn't cleaned the kit, choosing to risk the wrath of the capricious and vengeful gods of on call in favour of half an hour longer in the land of nod.

It felt as though my head had only just touched the pillow when the on-call phone rang. Again. I was catapulted out of slumber, bright flashes of annoyance surging through my sleep-deprived body, as I groped for the phone on my bedside table, fighting the urge to smash it for good measure. This was getting beyond a joke.

Thankfully I didn't recognise the number, so Kev was saved from being on the receiving end of my furious rant.

"Oakbank vets, emergency," I answered trying to sound more awake than I felt and hoping it was something that didn't require much in the way of thought.

A few weeks ago, I had a call at one o'clock in the morning from someone whose bearded dragon hadn't eaten in two days. Although it had taken all my strength to resist the urge to tell him he was an idiot, it didn't require me to leave my bed. Sometimes reptiles wouldn't eat for a day or two. If he had done any research at all before acquiring the animal, he would have known it was perfectly normal. I would never understand why people were looking at their animals at that hour of the morning, or why they suddenly felt the need to ring the vet for something that could very easily wait until normal business hours.

"My dog's bleeding," a slightly hysterical female voice informed me from the other end of the phone line.

An immediate kick of adrenaline had me sitting bolt upright in bed, already looking around for where I had deposited my clothes.

"How long has the dog been bleeding? Where is he bleeding from? How much blood has he lost?" despite my exhaustion and the lateness of the hour my brain was functioning at near crystal clarity. Adrenaline was a wonderful thing, something that most vets had to survive on at some point in their career.

My heart was pounding hard against my sternum and I wondered whether it was possible for it to bruise in doing so. I'd never done a blood transfusion before, where would I even get blood or blood products at this hour should it be required?

"Well," the hysteria had subsided somewhat, leaving a far more thoughtful tone, and the vague sense that this was *not* the emergency I had initially suspected trickled down my spine. "He's got this lump and it's kind of oozing."

I blinked, thinking that I'd just had some kind of aural hallucination. She had *not* just said she'd rung the *emergency* vet at two in the morning because her dog had an oozing lump.

"Pardon?" I tried to sound polite, but I knew my voice was hoarse with the strain of not emitting the hysterical laughter boiling in my throat.

"He's had this lump for a few weeks and now it's oozing," she informed me earnestly, her tone making me want to reach through the phone line and slap some sense into her.

"Is he well in himself?" I tried to determine the reason for her phone call. "How much blood has he lost?"

"Oh, he's fine! He's bouncing like he usually does. It's just oozing all over my cream carpets and I've got an estate agent coming around to take pictures of the house tomorrow afternoon! I can't have blood on my carpets, how will that look in the photos?"

Just shoot me now. I face-palmed, not even caring if the ridiculous woman on the other end of the phone heard me. How stupid could you be?

Would you ring for an ambulance or an emergency doctor's appointment because of an oozing lump? No. So why would you ring the vet for the same in the early hours of the morning?

"Alright, well as he's not bleeding a lot, I think it can wait until the practice opens in the morning," I honestly tried to keep the smothering sarcasm from my tone, but I don't think I was too successful. Thankfully it seemed to go completely over her head. "Here's what you need to do; get a cold cloth and apply pressure to the area that's oozing. I want you to do that for me until the practice opens at nine o'clock, then give us another ring and we'll arrange an appointment to get him seen."

"Oh, oh right," she sounded much too enthusiastic for the hour. "I'll just do that, thanks!"

And then she hung up.

I blinked at the phone for several long moments, not really wanting to believe that had just happened. I probably shouldn't have told the woman to apply pressure to an oozing lump for the next six hours, but I admit her ridiculous view of what consisted of an actual *emergency* combined with my lack of sleep had annoyed me sufficiently that I just couldn't help myself. Well it wouldn't do for such utter stupidity to go without some form of reward now, would it?

Falling back onto my pillows I flung the phone in the vague direction of the nightstand, and closed my eyes, praying for a few hours of peace and quiet. Sometimes the worst part of this job wasn't the physically gruelling tasks, or the emotional roller-coaster of life and death that we oftentimes rode on a daily basis. No, the worst part was dealing with the utter idiocy of the general public.

CHAPTER SEVENTEEN

February... run ins with the emergency services

February was a dark, dismal month of terrible weather and busy on call. After the January lull, small animal work had picked up momentum, along with the usual busyness of farm calls, the beginning of foaling season only added to the chaotic shift of my work-life balance. *Life?* What's that? I existed in an exhausting cycle of work, on call and the occasional night of sleep interspersed in between.

It was late on a Monday evening when I received a call from a local breeder of Miniature Shetland Ponies, to go to the aid of a mare in difficulty. Although I had never been to see this particular client before, I was relieved I already knew exactly where I was going; I drove past the field containing his ponies every day on my way to work, watching their little bellies gradually swelling with a sense of encroaching dread.

Foaling mares was a task far more fraught with difficulties than merely attending a farm to calve a cow. In their own right, horses of any description were far more fragile creatures than the inherent hardiness of a cow. I had seen cows fall over during caesareans, roll around in the muck and straw on their internal organs, and go on to recover completely, without even the blink of an eye. In a similar situation, a horse would probably expire immediately on the spot, or at least die several days later due to raging peritonitis.

Not only were they more likely to take harm in any given

circumstance, their uteruses were far more muscular and less flexible than those belonging to their bovine counterparts. It was true that the uterine contraction of a mare could potentially break a man's arm, and I was just accident prone enough to believe it would most likely happen to *me* if it was going to happen to anyone.

My third, and final reason for dreading this call, was that at least when I went to see a cow, I knew she would be appropriately restrained. Either she would be confined within a crush or pinned behind a gate with suitable protection from kicks or wallops or other traumatic injuries. A cow's kick could travel at ten miles an hour, which, believe me, hurt a great deal, but a horse's was a lot faster, and they were, for the most part, poorly restrained and capable of doing a lot of damage to the poor, unfortunate vet trying to help them.

I turned up to the field where I had been instructed to meet our client and was relieved to see Mr Berry's white van already waiting for me. He was a rough-looking older gentleman who looked as though his lined, craggy features had been cut and hewn by the harsh winds that could sweep through this part of the world. But I knew he loved his little horses to distraction, and his appearance was deceiving. He was, in actual fact, a rather gentle, kindly man.

Between the two of us we spent about twenty minutes attempting to capture the little pony, who only came up to just above my knees, as she trotted away from us, the head of her foal flopping limply from her back end. I admit I wasn't much help in the process, stumbling and tripping over hidden dips and holes, but at least I only fell on my face once or twice and I didn't break anything.

Once the pony was corralled and Mr Berry managed to get a head collar onto her, we spent another ten minutes persuading the stubborn, distressed creature that she really did want to walk the half mile back up the field toward the gate where I had left my car and equipment. It wasn't an easy task, as despite her small size, she was a difficult animal to move where she didn't want to go. I ended up grasping hold of her long tail and practically dragging her, along with steady pressure on the lead-rope, back up the hill.

By the time we'd got her where we wanted her, I was sweating profusely within the greenhouse of my waterproofs, despite the chilly, icy temperature, and had to pause to strip off a few of my layers so I didn't expire from heat exhaustion.

It didn't take long to ascertain that the foal was already dead. The baby didn't respond at all to my forceful pinch of its nostrils, nor when I gently poked its open, glassy eye – the corneal reflex generally the last thing to go before an animal died. Although this was not a good eventuality for Mr Berry, or the mare, it did make my life a little bit easier.

With these miniature ponies there was very little room to manoeuvre inside them. If there was a dystocia – a problem with the positioning of the foal – it was incredibly difficult to correct it when the foal was still alive. Their limbs were so long in comparison to those of a calf or a lamb, there was a real risk of inadvertently tearing through the muscles of the uterus in an attempt to place them into a more natural position. And this particular presentation; with only the head having passed through the pelvic canal was one of the most complicated to correct, eclipsed only by the utter dread of having a breach presentation.

Oftentimes, due to the stress and potential constriction of the narrowness of the pelvis in comparison to the head, and the drying out of foetal fluids, the head could swell making it very difficult to push it back into the uterus and arrange the feet and head into a more appropriate configuration. And, of course, you also had to take into account the hindrance of an agitated, stressed and occasionally angry mare while attempting to achieve this miraculous feat.

As there was no real danger to the already deceased foal at this point, I elected to sedate the mare, who had really not appreciated my brief investigation of the problem and was already being free and loose with her tiny, but painful, hooves. By the dubious, wavering light of a mobile phone I somehow managed to hit a vein first time, giving her a good dose of sedative to enable me to go about my business without the worry of her moving at an inadvisable moment, potentially injuring herself as well as me. I wanted to do a little happy dance at the momentous achievement of giving intravenous medication to a *Shetland* without having to struggle for hours to even find the jugular vein.

Adrenaline was an awesome hormone, it enabled you to achieve things you would never think possible in any normal situation.

While the mare was getting good and sleepy, I opened the gate and drove my car inside the field – securely closing it after I had done so, since we didn't need the rest of the ponies escaping onto the busy bypass – leaving the headlights turned on so I would have at least a little light to work by. It wasn't the most ideal of situations, but emergency call outs generally weren't. A vet had to be very flexible and rather creative with the equipment available if they were going to have any success out on farm calls.

Now that the mare was out cold, a towel thrown over her head to prevent the light from the headlights causing stimulation and making her kick out, my task was relatively simple, if a little bit gruesome.

"You're not bothered by blood, are you?" I asked Mr Berry before I began, really not wanting to deal with a fainting farmer on top of everything else.

There was a reason I was a vet, it meant I didn't have to deal with people ailments.

"Nah," he retorted. "Seen it aplenty afore, pet."

"Alright then, here we go."

Armed with my trusty scalpel blade I crouched beside the tail head against the mare's back; even though she was sedated it was best to be safe rather than sorry, and kneeling around an animal this size was a definite no-no. Grasping the head under the chin, I moved it into a position of full extension, thereby exposing the soft tissues of its throat. A long, confident incision cut through the skin, muscle and other soft tissue structures between the outside world and the trachea, dark, oxygen-deprived blood gushing out onto the damp, muddy grass. The windpipe itself was a tougher customer to severe. I palpated the space between a couple of the thick, rigid cartilage rings and used the sharp point of my instrument to make a deep stab that would enable me to work around the structure until it was fully detached.

I was in the process of concentrating on this trickier task, my head bent low over the foal's head so I could see what I was doing, when I heard my companion give a startled grunt.

"Wha the hell?" he exclaimed.

Surprised I lifted my head to see two dark shapes wearing bulky clothing moving toward us, torches shining on the ground as they picked their way over the uneven surface of the field. The blinding light from my headlights made it difficult to make out more than the height and shape of our visitors and I raised the bloodied hand holding the scalpel blade to shield my eyes and perhaps get a better view of who they were and what they wanted.

It wasn't until they were a bare few feet from where I was crouching, and Mr Berry was leaning on his mare to keep her immobilised, that I managed to make out the blue and silver POLICE insignia emblazoned across their chests. I couldn't help the hard rush of air that left my lungs nor the shock that stilled my mind for several long moments. I couldn't believe this was happening to me again. Were they following me around or something?

My friends would get a proper kick out of this situation. I was the only one among my peers who had any kind of run in with the police as yet, and now to have *another* one, well it would undoubtedly do the rounds for years. Exchanging our humorous, and not so humorous, adventures among ourselves was often helpful in maintaining a cheerful outlook on life and bolster sometimes severely strained moral.

"What's going on here?" one of the police officers asked in a gruff, suspicious manner, flicking his torch over the downed mare, the semi-decapitated foal, and my bloody, guilty hands.

I didn't recognise his voice, which was most likely the reason they had stopped in the first place. I suspected the previous police officers I had encountered had made a mental note of my car registration and wouldn't have stopped had they seen it parked in the middle of a field at oh dark thirty with the lights blazing.

I realised I hadn't released the head when they had approached, exposing the dark mess of severed flesh to their gazes and quickly let it go as though it burned. Unfortunately, this precipitated another rush of dark blood onto the grass and made a disgusting, slurping noise as the tissues slapped against one another.

"Me mare's foalin'," Mr Berry answered gruffly when it became apparent that the silence between the four of us was going to stretch on for several heartbeats too long. "Vet's fixing it, as yer can see."

I smiled pleasantly as their torch beams swept over the scene in front of them, still apparently dubious whether they should believe us or not. I helpfully brandished my gore-covered hand, still grasping the scalpel blade and watched as the younger, and I am assuming junior, member of the pair paled quite considerable.

"Foal's dead," I supplied with a quick grin, my mouth overtaken by some mischievous imp and unable to prevent myself from having a little bit of fun at their expense. "So, I'm cutting off its head to make it easier to get the rest of the body out. You can give us a hand if you want to make yourself useful."

My kind offer made the younger officer blanch even further and shoot a desperate glance at his companion. The older officer swiftly shook his head and began to back away from me as though I had just offered to cut off *his* head.

"No, that's fine," he said in a rush and I saw him swallow manfully. "You just carry on with what you're doing."

They practically ran back to their police car and drove away faster than was perhaps strictly necessary. I shrugged, shooting my companion a sly glance as I got back down to business.

"Gud on yer, pet," Mr Berry muttered with a grin. "Pokin' their noses inta other people's doin's."

In actuality the police *were* performing a useful service, as it wasn't uncommon for animals and expensive pieces of farm equipment to go missing from the rural community. It was especially a problem in the build up to the Appleby Horse Fair in June when the Travelling community came through the area. I knew they were just doing their jobs, but I hadn't been able to help myself.

After that interruption I made quick work of bisecting the trachea and freeing the soft tissue up to the limit of the spinal cord. Bending the foal's chin toward its chest I inserted the point of the blade into the space between the second and third cervical vertebrae, cutting through the last remaining connections of head to neck. The head came away easily in my hand and I discarded it a little distance behind me, making a mental note to collect it before we departed. It wouldn't do to leave a horse head behind in the field.

Carefully storing my scalpel blade, I grasped the exposed neck and with the application of lube and a bit of muscle, pushed the foal deeper into the body of the mare. Without the head it was a relatively simple task to be able to grasp the front feet, cupping my hand over the sharper points of the little hooves to guide them up into the pelvic canal to prevent any damage to the womb from occurring. Once both front feet were exteriorised, I slipped ropes onto the legs and setting my heels into the ground used my body weight to apply traction to those protruding limbs. More lube and a bit of forceful persuasion later and the foal engaged within the pelvis. A bit more lubrication, and a few moments of jiggling and force, and the troublesome baby slid free.

In the rush of movement, I sat back heavily onto my backside, almost end up on my back as the momentum carried me backward. A gush of fluid followed the limp body of the foal turning the ground beneath the mare into a boggy quagmire. As gently as possible I inserted my hand into the mare, grasping the foetal membranes that hadn't emerged with the foal and with firm, but gentle traction pulled them free of their moorings deep within the uterus. Turning so the headlights could illuminate the entirety of the placenta I checked it was all present and correct – retained foetal membranes in mares could be a very severe complication – before quickly checking there were no tears or other damage internally to the mare.

Satisfied that all was as it should be, I drew up and administered pain relief and antibiotics to the still groggy mare, before going about the gruesome business of collecting the pieces of the foal into a rubble bag Mr Berry had taken from his van for this exact purpose. We remained there for several moments to ensure the mare got back onto her feet, and once she had, parted ways.

It wasn't the best outcome; that would have been both a live foal and a well mare, but it was the best outcome that could be expected in the circumstances. I was satisfied I had done my best, and I would have yet another entertaining tale to regale my colleges and friends with.

My next encounter with the country's emergency services was quite a bit more serious than the one before.

At the end of surgery one evening we received a call from a client reporting their male cat hadn't passed urine in over twenty-four hours. She was immediately instructed to bring the animal to the practice, as blocked bladder in a feline was a distinct emergency.

A complete urethral obstruction can happen suddenly, and is life-threatening; therefore, immediate treatment is necessary. A combination of crystal precipitates and protein can form a urethral plug and cause a complete blockage of the urethra. Kidney failure can occur within 36-48 hours of complete urethral obstruction and may prove fatal in less than 72 hours without veterinary intervention. This condition is seen in male cats, due to a number of contributing factors that is not fully understood. Diet and obesity can play a part, as can other environmental or disease factors such as cancers or previous injury. The most common individual this condition is seen in is male, black and white, neutered cats that are overweight and on high protein diets.

"He's very distressed," the owner said breathlessly as she rushed her pet into my consulting room, depositing the plastic cat carrier on my table. "He's usually such a loving, gentle cat, but he's completely changed!"

I felt a distinct sinking sensation in the pit of my stomach. Usually when owners referred to their animals as loving and gentle it meant that actually the cat was a feral tiger that had been shrunk in the wash.

Such was the case for this particular cat.

Just as I was about to open the carrier door a vicious paw struck violently at the plastic bars, narrowly missing several sharp talons being sunk into the back of my hand. A loud, snarling yowl rose from the darkened depths of the cat cage and I exchanged a glance with Jess, who was the nurse on with me this evening. Neither of us felt the need to exchange any words.

"I'll just go get the crush cage," she said, disappearing into the back of the practice to collect the aforementioned item.

A 'crush cage' was generally a wire cage that also contained a second wall on a moveable arm that enabled the vet to squash the cat up against one side of the box to easily administer sedation to the fractious animal, without risking life or limb. Unfortunately, there still remained the difficulty of extracting the cat from one carrier and getting it into the other.

The usual technique was to upend the starting point carrier and allow gravity to work its magic in ushering the animal to its final destination. However, that is often easier said than done.

We managed to get the carrier door open without any overt gouging of flesh, but that was where everything started to go wrong. Before we could tip cat into the crush cage, the outraged feline burst from its confinement, mouth open and talons extended ready to sink into the nearest fleshy surface. Unfortunately, that nearest fleshy surface happened to be my right wrist and then subsequently my left elbow.

Blood was streaming from both my arms by the time I managed to disengage from the vicious, snarling creature, slamming the lid shut on the crush cage, despite the violent shaking of my own hands. The pungent aroma of feline urine immediately filled the room and I looked at the floor to see a large puddle of amber liquid quickly mingling with the equally expansive pool of claret that was forming at my feet.

Well, at least we had managed to solve one problem.

Immediately my teeth dug into the inside of my lip, the extra bite of self-inflicted pain giving me something else to focus on aside from the sharp, throbbing sting of my wounds. It would not do for me to stand crying in front of the client. Jess sent me out of the room with a demanding tilt of her head while she rapidly got rid of the client.

She found me bent over the sink, my head hanging low as I ran almost scalding water over the deep bite-marks on my inner wrist and inner elbow, trying to stop the tears that streamed down my cheeks and prevent myself from vomiting into the basin with a combination of shock and pain. Her hands were gentle as she poured surgical scrub to my wounds, cleaning them as carefully as possible, but it did nothing to help me cease crying. Bandages were efficiently applied, and then we were immediately off to the local *Casualty* department.

It is always important to seek medical attention after receiving a cat bite. Cats carry many different bacteria in their mouths, and up to 80% of cat bites can lead to infection if they are not treated appropriately. These wounds, although often less serious than those inflicted by a dog, can be far more difficult to medicate and even debride if necessary, and if involving a joint can develop into osteomyelitis, a serious infection of the bone. As it was almost seven o'clock in the evening and no doctors were open, it was off to A&E we went.

We sat there for almost three hours before I was called into a

---

consulting room to be reviewed by the nurse practitioner. She unwrapped my bandages, examined and cleaned my, by now very swollen and angry, wounds with gentle sympathy and several soft clucking exhalations of concern. They were re-wrapped with an iodine dressing and I was about to be sent on my way when I opened my mouth to exclaim.

"You're not going to give me any antibiotics?" I queried in astonishment. Considering the volume of cat bite abscesses we saw coming through our doors on a monthly basis, I was frankly flabbergast that they weren't going to give me at least a broad spectrum dose of antibiotics to prevent this deep and ugly wound from developing into something worse.

"The wound has been well cleaned," the nurse returned with a frown. "And shouldn't cause any further complications."

I understood she was harried and rushed off her feet with a busy waiting room and several emergencies that had arrived while I had been waiting, but that didn't negate my desire to receive the appropriate medication. I crossed my arms, unable to hide my wince as doing so aggravated the wound on my elbow.

"I disagree," I didn't mean for my tone to sound antagonistic, but I was tired, sore and hungry. "We would always advise someone who has been bitten by a cat to get antibiotics from their doctor; especially in a case such as this were the cat itself might also have an infection."

Her eyebrows shot up her forehead so high they became at one with her hairline.

"I'm a vet," I answered her silent question. Usually I didn't go around broadcasting my profession, because it tended to lead to people asking me questions about their pets, but in this case I thought it was a warranted revelation. "And I'm not leaving until you give me antibiotics."

We argued about it for several long moments, until the nurse threw up her hands with a disgruntled;

"Fine!"

She left the room for a couple of minutes and then returned with a prescription of potentiated amoxicillin. I took it with a quiet thank you and returned to the waiting room where Jess was waiting to take me home.

"That took you long enough," she remarked as we departed the hospital.

"She wasn't going to give me antibiotics," I supplied.

"Idiot," Jess returned derisively.

I awoke the next morning feeling sore and off colour. After using a pair of arm-length rectal gloves so I could shower and not get my bandages wet, I managed to choke down a bit of breakfast, even though I really didn't feel like it, and drove into work. Peeling off the bandages, thinking that I would replace the iodine dressing from the night before with a Manuka honey one from the practice's supplies – Manuka honey was an exceptionally good antiseptic – I blanched at the furious red streaks that were progressing up my arm toward my heart. They had definitely not been there the night before and were the dreadful harbingers of septicaemia should I not seek immediate treatment.

Quickly re-bandaging after showing my new angry accessories to Andrew, I took myself to the doctors where I was prescribed a course of metronidazole on top of the potentiate amoxicillin I was already taking. The friendly young doctor got a serious look on his face as he cautioned me that if it didn't improve in the next few days I might have to be admitted to hospital for intravenous antibiotics.

The metronidazole made me feel as sick as a dog, sicker than the infection had, but at least the red lines on my arms began to regress and I didn't have to go into hospital. A cautionary tale, if any was required, just how dangerous cats could really be.

CHAPTER EIGHTEEN

March... I've never been so clean, and yet so dirty!

March came upon us with a rush of new life, and the dismal disappointment that the snow still hadn't left. I was left a little bewildered at just where February had disappeared to and astonished I had been in clinical practice for just shy of a year. It had all gone so quickly, the experiences of the previous eleven months a jumbled mess of thoughts, achievements and failures. I probably should have been quietly confident in all I had learned since I had moved to the North East, all of which proved I could perform in a profession that had been my heart's desire since I was barely old enough to go to school. March tested my abilities and knowledge honed over the past eleven months, but showed I still had a lot to learn in my profession.

But I wasn't going to let it get me down, even if it did occasionally make me worried.

A couple of weeks into the month I was called out to visit my old friend Mr Gill of Brookbank Place at about five o'clock in the morning to attend a lambing. I didn't find out until I rocked up on the farm that it was a rotten lambing. Joy of joys.

The ewe wasn't the healthiest looking of specimens, an unusual case for this particular establishment, as all his stock were, if anything, too fit. She was down on her side at one end of the barn, her breathing fast and shallow, and her eyes sunken into her grey-flecked head. A quick assessment of her broken, missing teeth told me immediately she was an older ewe, the thickness of her fleece belying her thin frame. She was what a stockman would classify as 'broken mouthed' meaning that she had lost some of her incisors, quite normal in older sheep, making her less able of masticating food and less likely to keep weight on and adequately nurture her lambs. This usually occurred around six years of age and was a sure indicator that she would be marked as a cull ewe and sent to the abattoir instead of being retained for breeding the following year.

If she survived this experience.

I was happy to see that it wasn't Specks, the first caesarean of my professional career, and a sheep I had an inexplicable fondness for.

"She's usually the last to the trough," Mr Gill said sadly as he knelt beside the beleaguered ewe, one hand gently petting the animal's head. "But when she didn't appear at all this morning, I was worried. I checked her and what's coming out the back end is pretty foul stuff."

Unlike usual for a lambing or calving, I pulled on a pair of arm length gloves, plus a pair of latex gloves before I began my investigation of what was going on inside this ewe. Normally I eschewed wearing gloves in this situation, due to the simple fact that these gloves were made for the typical male farm vet and the fingers were almost three times too big for my tiny hands. I always found they were more of a hindrance than a help, the too long fingers creating an impediment to my ability to manoeuvre a foetus around an abdomen, but in this instance I wasn't going to delve inside without some form of protection. Rotting lambs processed a particularly pungent odour that somehow managed to cling to your hands for days on end, even after multiple washings, usually most noticeable when you were trying to eat, and I wanted to avoid that eventuality as much as possible.

This discharge coming from the back end of this sheep was especially unpleasant. She must have either aborted several days previously, or the lamb had been mal-presented not coming into the pelvic canal and thus encouraging uterine contractions. In either event the lamb was definitely a number of days dead and very malodourous.

I managed to get hold of a foot and a head, gently coaxing both up into the pelvic canal. The foot was soft, the horn of the hoof coming apart in my hands as I manoeuvred the limb. A little gentle traction had the oedematous skin that crackled with air that had collected under the skin with the effects of decomposition slough away in my grasp. A little more tension had the entire limb almost effortlessly separating from the shoulder and coming away in my hand.

I sat back on my heels and looked at the appendage in my grip with a disgusted wince. A sigh rippled through me as I glanced at Mr Gill. His expression was a little nonplussed.

"I guess this little one is coming out in pieces then," I said, injecting a little light-hearted, gruesome humour into my tone. It was very easy to become disconcerted or depressed by the goriness of the profession if you didn't find amusement in the situation.

I dived back inside and managed to manoeuvre the head into the pelvis, sinking my fingertips into its mushy eye-sockets to get a good grip on the skull. The head was smaller than I would expect of a full-term lamb, and I suspected there had been a problem with the pregnancy, hence the abortion and our current situation. If the lamb was this small the ewe should have had no difficulty in passing it normally.

As I was tugging on the head, I felt something give, the skull separating from the rest of its slightly swollen, disintegrating corpse. I withdrew my hand, complete with skull, which I brandished somewhat theatrically at my companion.

"This lamb is very dead," I said somewhat unnecessarily. "You've not had any other problems with aborting ewe?"

"Alas, poor Yoric," Mr Gill returned with a small grin, and then became serious again as he added. "No more than normal."

It wasn't abnormal for a flock to suffer an abortion rate of approximately 2%, due to non-infectious factors such as adverse weather, a foetus being non-compatible with life, or the mother developing an infection or fever during pregnancy. We only became worried if a farm began to experience a number of events in rapid progression, generally referred to as a 'storm', which could be caused by a number of infectious diseases that were bad news for a farmer's bottom line.

The lamb turned out to be one of a set of triplets, accounting for its lower than normal birth weight. Both of its siblings were also in a delicate state, meaning I had to remove all three in small sections, taking far longer than a normal lambing usually would. By the time I finished I was covered in foul-smelling uterine fluids and in desperate need of a shower. It was lucky I had a relatively poor sense of smell; otherwise I didn't think I'd be able to stand the smell of myself.

Before I left the farm, I filled the poor, sickly ewe with fluids via a stomach tube, antibiotics and anti-inflammatories in the hope she would pull through. Unfortunately, if sheep are known for one thing, it's their ability to die. It has been stated by more than one person that a sheep's main aim in life is to die as quickly as possible after their birth. The prognosis didn't look good for this ewe, but when I warned Mr Gill of the likelihood of her not surviving he simply shrugged.

"It is what it is," he said in a matter-of-fact manner. "At least we've given her a fighting chance."

We parted ways and half an hour later I was just stepping out of the shower when the on-call phone rang again. It was now seven o'clock in the morning and I still hadn't had any breakfast. Trying not to drip water all over the bathroom I answered the call, dreading what it might be. I had a feeling in the pit of my stomach it wasn't going to be anything good.

"We've got a horse colicking," Mr Collins of Hole Hill Farm informed me abruptly in lieu of a greeting.

The Collinses were beef farmers who were active participants in the Braes of Derwent Hunt, and I knew they kept a few horses, but it was still a surprise to be called out there for something other than a bovine problem. Mr Collins Snr was a gruff, abrupt man in his late sixties, who I'd never quite been able to work out whether he liked me, or merely tolerated me, and who always seemed to make me feel inadequate whenever I went up to their place. I mentally cursed that the call hadn't come in a couple of hours later so Andrew could have gone up there to deal with him, Mr Collins always seemed to prefer him to attend anyway.

"Right," I returned in a brisk, business-like tone as I discretely tried to dry myself while talking, and not revealing that was what I was doing. "I'll be there in fifteen minutes."

The farm was on the other side of Lanchester, going up the hill in the direction of civilisation, and it wouldn't take me too long to get there. I pulled on my clothes, did a cursory dry of my wet, unruly hair, fed the cat and the rabbit and ate a banana on the way to my car. I couldn't function without eating something in the morning, an empty stomach often making me feel nauseous and light-headed. I had never been able to understand how people managed to work and be rational, productive people without breakfast.

Arriving on farm I was directed around to the stables in the opposite direction I usually took to deal with the cattle. The horse in question belonged to the partner of Mr Collins Jr, and was a tall, handsome bay whose coat was soaked and lathered with heavy sweat, his nostrils wide and dilated as he pawed at the floor and intermittently kicked at his heaving belly. The disturbed sawdust of his bed showed evidence that he had been down more than once overnight, and I felt an uncomfortable tickle in the pit of my stomach that this wasn't going to be an easy case of slightly overzealous guts.

Under Mr Collins' watchful, judgemental gaze I performed a quick clinical exam, deftly avoiding the shifting, agitated bulk of the horse as he danced in place. With each abnormal parameter my chest grew even tighter. I hesitantly performed a rectal examination, something I usually eschewed in horses unless I couldn't physically help it. It was entirely possible to cause more harm than good with such a procedure in horses as sometimes the rectum would tear during the examination, which was pretty much as good as a bullet between the eyes for the horse. My exploration revealed distended loops of small intestine, like inflated pieces of bicycle inner-tube at the tips of my fingers and I bit my lip unhappily, relieved to at least see no blood on the glove when I withdrew my arm.

This was not good.

"He's got some distended guts," I informed Mr Collins, trying not to wince at the way his eyes narrowed slightly. "Which is probably why he's been so uncomfortable overnight. I think this might be something a little more serious than what we usually see. It might be necessary to refer him."

"I'd rather not," Mr Collins retorted gruffly. "Isn't there something you can do?"

He left it unsaid that he didn't think my diagnosis was to his liking, and that he didn't quite believe that I knew what I was talking about.

"We can give him some pain-relief and some buscopan to settle his guts," I responded as professionally as I could. "I'm going to pass a stomach tube to see if he's got any reflux. Some fluids will help as well."

As I left the stable to gather my equipment, I thought I heard a snort, emanating from the man, not the horse, and tried to not allow his attitude to distress me. When I returned with the soft rubber tube, a funnel and some lectade – an electrolyte solution – Mr Collins had already provided me with a few buckets of lukewarm water. Administering a small dose of a sedative to hopefully ensure the horse's cooperation, and because xylazine had an analgesic effect on the abdominal viscera, I began to insert the tube.

Unlike with cattle stomach-tubing, a horse was a slightly more delicate procedure. The soft rubber tube is inserted into the nasal passage and advanced slowly in an upward direction, without applying any force should resistance be encountered. Most horses will swallow the tube voluntarily once it reaches the level of the epiglottis, allowing the tube to pass down the oesophagus, where it is visible in the neck. It is possible for the tube to pass into the trachea, and it's always important to ensure this doesn't occur as aspiration of fluids can lead to pneumonia or death. Entering the stomach requires the vet to blow into the tube, and because of this most vets hold the end of the rubber tube in their mouths whilst placing the stomach tube.

To obtain reflux the tube must become a siphon by creating a complete tube of water from the stomach to the end of the tube. This required the most disgusting aspect of this whole procedure. To create that siphon it was necessary to first fill the tube with water, either using a syringe, or pouring water through a funnel into the tube held above head-height and then sucking on the end of the tube to encourage the flow of the stomach contents. It wasn't an uncommon occurrence to get a mouthful of gastric acid in the process, which is a difficult thing to encounter without wanting to vomit.

Thankfully, this time I managed to time it right and directed the tube into an empty bucket before the contents of the stomach could gush into my mouth. However, that didn't necessarily mean I didn't end up splattered with the off-green, disgusting smelling rush of fluid that followed. A steady stream of gastric juice followed, and when that flow finished, I dunked the end of the tube into a jug of clean water and once again put it into my mouth, grimacing as I did so at the left-over flavour of the stomach contents that lingered on the rubber.

We repeated this process several more times, my stomach turned a little more each time I put the tube into my mouth, until we finally couldn't get any further reflux from the horse. A normal horse should produce approximately two litres of reflux, indicating that the stomach was emptying normally into the small intestine. By my reckoning, taking into account the fluid that had spilled onto the floor – and me – we were closer to five litres than to two.

This horse had an obstruction. Just as I had feared.

I glanced at Mr Collins, whose mouth was set in a grim line and buried my wince. The horse most likely needed to be referred to a hospital environment, at least for medical management, if not surgery if the problem was severe enough, but I doubted we were going to go down that route.

"Without further imaging I can't tell you exactly what's wrong," I informed the farmer reluctantly. "But he's definitely seriously unwell. I suspect there's a blockage in his small intestine since that's more reflux than we would normally see. We'll give him some fluids and some pain relief, but if he doesn't respond, we'll have to reconsider whether we want to refer him or not."

My only response was a grunt. So, I got on with the job of funnelling a couple of litres of warm water plus electrolyte solution into the unfortunate animal and gave some pain relief intravenously. In this situation I used a drug called *Ketofen*. It wasn't the strongest pain relief I had in my car, but I didn't want to mask the painful symptoms of the condition, potentially leading us to think the horse was improving when he was actually not.

I left Mr Collins with an inscrutable expression of his face and pointed my car back down the hill into the village. Although it was now past nine o'clock, and the surgery was open, I rang through to inform them I was heading home for a shower, since I stunk of horse stomach juices, and some breakfast before coming into work.

Thirty minutes later I had barely crossed the threshold of the practice when I was told to turn around and head back out the way I had come. There was another horse colicking up at the Riding's and Andrew was already due to go out to a bullock that had broken its leg, requiring a vet's presence to write an emergency slaughter certificate.

It took me twenty minutes to drive out to the farm, and I was greeted by the farmer's daughter, whose horse it was, with a worn, worried expression on her face. Samantha – Sam – Riding had several dogs who never seemed to be out of the practice for one reason or another, and I knew her well enough by now to understand that she wasn't one to over-exaggerate a problem. If she thought the horse was in dire need, then it likely was.

Jeremy, the piebald cob, was indeed looking exceptionally sorry for himself. I completed another swift clinical exam, this time finding that his guts were moving slower than normal, and, after gritting my teeth at the thoughts of performing yet another rectal exam, I discovered the source of his problem was an impaction of his colon at the level of the pelvic flexure.

The pelvic flexure is an area of the colon that in a horse bends at an almost right angle, and because of this turn is a common cause of colic in the horse. Impactions at this level of the intestine are usually caused by poorly digested food, ingestion of sand and other alterations in management or disease. Usually treatment for this condition is medical by the provision of fluids, pain relief and laxatives, which is generally very effective, although in some cases surgical correction of the impaction is necessary.

Unfortunately, although it is relatively easy to diagnose a pelvic flexure impaction on rectal exam, it is difficult to do so for impactions of the right dorsal colon, which is a more serious problem.

In this case, armed with my diagnosis, I set about administering my treatment. Intravenous pain relief was easily provided; fluids and laxatives unfortunately required me to pass my second stomach tube of the day.

This time it didn't quite go as easily as the first. Jeremy tossed his head at an inopportune moment causing my grip on the tube to slip, and a nose-bleed of mammoth proportions to ensue, which meant that both Sam and I were liberally doused in claret by the time we had finished. And then came the liquid paraffin laxative application.

There are various recommendations for the volume of laxative required to correct this problem, anywhere between five and ten litres. Trying to get even the lower volume through a tube the diameter of a man's thumb is not a tidy endeavour. Paraffin and blood do not a good combination make.

I left Sam after about half an hour of fighting to get enough laxative into her recalcitrant horse, with even more paraffin to administer orally over the next forty-eight hours and, after consulting reception to ensure there were no further calls for me to attend, returned home for my third shower and change of clothing of that day. It wasn't even lunch time yet.

After that call I managed to spend an hour in the practice before a call came in to replace a prolapsed uterus in a cow. Gobbling down a portion of my lunch, because I knew I probably wouldn't get back to the practice in time to eat much before afternoon surgery began, I climbed into my car and headed out. I hoped this was the last of my calls for the day, because I was running low on clean waterproofs after my previous three visits, and because of the cold weather it was going to be difficult to get them dry enough to be of any use in such a short period of time.

When I got to the farm the cow in question was down in the crush and didn't look as though she was going to get back to her feet any time soon. Not only that, the crush itself was an older version of the breed and exceptionally narrow, making it difficult to admit more than one small person behind the cow to manhandle the feet of flesh protruding from her vulva.

With an inward sigh I got down to work.

Using the available man-power – the farmer and one of his farm-hands – I got straps around the cow's hind feet and pulled them out from beneath her body so they were splayed out on either side of the prolapse, and I could comfortably – ahem – kneel between them to get access to the problem. A clean plastic sheet from the back of my car, kept specifically for these situations, was placed beneath the exposed flesh to protect it from the muddy ground, and a liberal application of warm soapy water helped to remove whatever contamination it had acquired from the environment. There was no use pushing potential infection back inside the cow when she was already at a distinct disadvantage. As the farmer looked on with an expectant expression – possibly expecting me to fail, because of my relative size compared to the task – I set my equipment out within easy reach; vulval suture tape, twelve-inch buhner needle and empty wine bottle, and got down to business. We had seen so many of these prolapses this year that I was an old hand at this procedure now.

A liberal application of lubrication later, I rested the mass of oozing flesh on my bent knees and began the arduous task of persuading it back into the cow's body, where it really didn't seem to want to go.

There was, truthfully, little in the way of actual *skill* involved in this procedure. All it required was patience, steady pressure and careful hands. There was no use pushing with fingers, as it was possible to tear into the flesh requiring sutures, or gripping the bulging caruncles that looked like pock-marked kidneys protruding from the smooth surface of the uterus, as these were relatively easy to tear from their slender, delicate stalks. Firm pressure with the flat of your hand, or with a closed fist was the order of the day.

By the time I had managed to get all but an approximately football-sized portion of the uterus back into the abdomen my arms and shoulders were screaming at the strain of the prolonged effort and my entire upper body was drenched with sweat and other less than pleasant fluids. I could feel them trickling down beneath my waterproofs and polo shirt, likely soaking all the way through to my bra.

There was only one positive aspect of being female in this situation; the boob shelf. It was quite useful to be able to prop the weight of the uterus on your chest, using it as a backup pressure to your hands to push the organ back where it belonged. However, this meant that you often ended up with uterus on your face.

But to be honest, by this point I'd had far worse things on my face.

I was just beginning to allow myself to think I was going to be successful, to think about getting the farmer to pass me my wine bottle, when the cow bellowed and heaved at the flesh I had been trying to return to its proper home. All that organ spat back out at me, its great weight impacting on my right shoulder, and since I was wedged in an awkward position within the crush, taking my shoulder with it.

Cruel, searing pain whipped through my body like lightning and I actually tasted blood in my mouth as my teeth bit into the inside of my cheek to prevent the cry that wanted to escape my lips being given life and breath. I saw dark spots dancing across my vision as agonised sensation crawled over my torso and up my neck like a thousand fire ants biting into my skin. My head dropped instinctively to cover the white-hot tears that leaked helplessly from the corners of my eyes.

I swallowed and swallowed again, my left arm and shoulder struggling with the strain of bearing the entire weight of the uterus, my right arm utterly useless. A steady litany of profanities fired like bullets from my mouth as I struggled against the urge to break down in tears. I refused to cry on farm. I refused to give any of our farmers evidence that I was just a little girl after all.

"Are you al-reet, pet?" the farm enquired worriedly after I had been knelt there motionless for several moments too long.

"Yep," I answered through gritted teeth, unable to help the hoarse quality of my voice. My right hand side had gone worryingly numb now, something I knew wasn't a good sign. "She just jarred me is all."

I took a deep breath and closing my eyes managed to get back into a reasonable position to deal with the problematic uterus. Movement made my abused right shoulder scream at me again, but I gritted my teeth harder and ignored the fiery flashes of pain and the ominous grinding sensation from within the joint itself in an attempt to get on with the job in hand.

Those were the longest fifteen minutes of my life; agony streaking through my body in continuous waves of hot torment. I was certain my companions were speaking to me, but I couldn't spare any attention to actually listen to what they were saying. All my brainpower was required for the arduous task of not crying.

I'm not sure how I managed it; physically my shoulder shouldn't have been capable of the motion and force required to shove that flesh back into the abdomen. But *finally* the entire uterus was where it belonged. This is when the wine bottle came in. It was a handy trick I'd picked up from a female vet of a similar size to me while I was seeing practice. Due to the relative disparity between the length of arm and the size of the uterus, it was difficult without some form of arm-extender to ensure the horns of the uterus were properly everted, therefore helping to prevent to cow from re-prolapsing. The smooth curve of the bottom of the bottle, and the long neck made a perfect tool for this job. Even if its presence as part of my kit made people look at me out of the side of their eyes.

Carting around empty wine bottles was not exactly *normal*.

It felt like a lifetime later that I had finally managed to stitch up her vulva, yet another aid to preventing re-prolapse, and I wanted to collapse to the floor in a puddle of misery, but I couldn't relax yet. Pain relief, antibiotics and some oxytocin to help invert the uterus needed to be applied. Usually I would whack a bottle of calcium solution beneath the skin as well, as calcium deficiency could contribute to uterine inertia and this problem in particular, but I just didn't have it in me to do so that day. Thankfully the farmer had his own butterfly valve – the device often used in this process – and I was happy to leave him with the bottle to get on with it himself.

Unfortunately, I had to get the farmer to hose me down while I scrubbed myself clean with Fam as I didn't have two properly functioning arms to hold both the hose and the brush. Each and every movement was scorching agony, but I persevered with gritted teeth and stubborn determination to not be mistaken for weak or fragile.

The comforting solitude of my car was a cocooning oasis. I drove out of the farmyard, parked a couple of hundred yards down the road so none of the farm workers would see me, and cried for a good ten minutes.

Another call to the practice to explain that I'd finished the call and was once again heading home for shower number four saw me on my way back to my house. A mouthful of painkillers and the hot water helped to ease some of my discomfort, but I still couldn't comfortably move my right shoulder, and lifting my arm anywhere near the level of my shoulder was the absolutely last thing I wanted to do in life.

I hindsight I probably ought to have gone to the doctor, or even A&E, my own medical knowledge sufficient to tell me I had done something serious to my body. But I have a slight phobia of human medical professionals, and we were far too busy for me to take the time off to get it sorted. I was hoping that if I just ignored it, and got on with work, then the injury would somehow miraculously fix itself.

Unfortunately, vets, for a group of medically minded people, are often less than sensible of their own good when it comes down to injuring themselves, or sickness. I've known vets come into work with broken bones, or pneumonia during busy periods because the practice would struggle to cope with a man down, or even just because they couldn't stand to be idle at home. Foolish perhaps, and not conducive to a healthy body certainly, but it's a staggeringly common phenomenon.

Upon my return to the practice my colleges obviously noticed there was something not quite right with me, but I brushed off their concerns with a shrug of my non-painful shoulder.

"I'm fine," I muttered when Nurse Gwen caught me rubbing uncomfortably at my injured limb and holding back tears after wrestling with a Jack Russel Terrier. "Just jarred my shoulder on that prolapse."

I could tell she didn't believe me, but since I stubbornly refused to admit there was anything wrong, there was little any of them could do about the problem.

Close to five o'clock that evening we received another call from Mr Collins of Hole Hill Farm. The horse hadn't improved. In fact, if anything he had deteriorated. Once again, we had the conversation about referral. Ten minutes later I went back out to the farm to put the horse to sleep.

Thankfully, Jeremy, my other colic of the day, made a full recovery, which is more than could be said for my shoulder. It wouldn't be until the end of lambing season, when I physically *couldn't* lift my arm above shoulder level, that I sought the opinion of a medical professional about my injury. I was informed I had a tear in my rotator cuff, which had subsequently caused soft tissue issues with the entirety of my shoulder girdle and the muscles supporting it. A referral to a physiotherapist was put into motion, but my shoulder would never be the same again.

CHAPTER NINETEEN

April ... Acceptance!

The beginning of April marked a full year since I had begun working at Oakbank Veterinary Surgery, a year packed full of lessons learned and roiling emotions. I was happy where I was working, and, unlike several of my friends who had already moved on from their first places of employment, I couldn't see myself going anywhere for the foreseeable future.

Life was good. I was taking the busy season of work in my stride, minus the continuing problems with my shoulder, but if I ignored them long enough I was hopeful they would eventually go away, and even the weather was taking a turn for the better. It no longer snowed every night, giving the white stuff already on the ground a chance to melt away for good. Grass was beginning to grow, finally farmers were able to kick their animals out onto pasture, easing the burden of stocking density within their sheds and reducing the incidences of pneumonia we were being faced with on an almost constant basis.

Having noticed I was struggling with the more physical aspects of the job after the infamous uterine prolapse, Andrew and Carl seemed to have come to a consensus that I was to be kept within the practice itself, dealing with the relatively less strenuous small animal case load, or the tedious but not tasking work of vaccinating horses, unless the number of calls demanded a second vet attend to them, or I was on call for the night. I was grateful for the reprieve, enjoying the opportunity to stay in out of the weather, which although improving was still pretty awful, and preventing my fingers from becoming frost-bitten.

I was just putting the final stitches into a cat spay when Leah poked her head around the corner with an expression on her face that was a cross between amusement and repulsion.

"We've got a call for you," she said. "The Brownlow's have a horse that's bitten off its own tongue."

I couldn't help but pull a disgusted face at the very thought. Just biting the inside of your own mouth was painful enough, I couldn't contemplate the pain of, or the mechanics of how the animal had managed such a strange feat. I downed my tools, leaving my patient to recover under the watchful eyes of the nurses and turned to Katie, the fourth-year vet student who was with us for the next couple of weeks during their Easter break.

"Would you like to come with me?" I asked, strangely amused by the circumstances. "I'm not certain you'll get a clinical case review out of it, but it just might prove interesting in any rate."

"I'll just go and get my boots," was her predictable response.

Katie was one of the better vet students who visited the practice on a semi-regular basis. She was knowledgeable, useful and didn't seem to mind the way I habitually entertained myself by gently torturing them. Not in a malicious manner, of course, but I was simply paying back the general tormenting that had been done to *me* as a student by the vets I had seen practice with. For the most part it consisted of asking questions of them whenever they asked me a question in an attempt to get them to answer their own query. My favourite past-time when with final year students, allowing them to operate on cat spays or castrates was, while they were concentrating every iota of their attention on the procedure they were performing, to casually ask whether their animal was still breathing. It usually made them jump and panic, and then swear at me when they realised I wasn't being serious, but even that light-hearted banter had a purpose. Even though there was generally a nurse present to monitor any anaesthetic in the majority of practices, it was still ultimately the vet's responsibility to ensure the animal was not compromised by the anaesthetic.

A short trip up the hill and we were pulling into the yard, Sarah Brownlow waiting for us just beyond the gate with an amused, but resigned expression on her features.

"Bloody stupid horse," she greeted us, pointing out a stable at the near end of the yard where several of her stable girls were gathered in a concerned multi-coloured flock. "He was so eager to get to his grub that he bit through his own tongue!"

"Has he severed it entirely?" I asked curiously as I followed her over to the source of the consternation.

"Not that we can see, but it's flopping about quite a lot. I don't see how you're going to reattach it, but at least he's not bleeding to death."

The crowd of concerned onlookers parted to allow us into the stable where one of the older stable hands was already waiting with the horse secured by a head collar to the wall. The floor of the stable was drenched in blood, a steady stream of rich crimson drops falling from the animal's mouth, and every time the chestnut gelding shook his head in discomfort, gouts of scarlet went flying everywhere, coating the walls, making it look as though someone had been murdered.

"This is Applejack," Sarah said with an exasperated huff. "He's more a clown than a horse, but he's pleasant softy, even if he's an idiot."

Thankfully the practice owned a Hausmann's gag, a special piece of equipment designed to hold a horses' mouth open so the mouth and teeth could be safely examined without the risk of losing a finger. It consisted of a bridle made from sturdy leather straps with two plates into which the upper and lower incisors fitted. A ratchet enabled the horses' mouth to be held open without risking the gag coming loose or closing on the operator's hand. Once this contraption was placed on the horse to my satisfaction, I reached into his mouth and grasped hold of his tongue, behind where he had made such a neat incision. The wound went through over three-quarters of the width of the tongue, at full thickness the entire way along. It was about an inch back from the tip, thankfully not extending to where the major vessels that supplied the tongue were located, as had he severed one or more of them then he would have stood a good chance of bleeding enough to compromise his circulatory system.

In truth the tip of the tongue was hanging on by a mere thread. No amount of epic, heroic surgery was going to save that vascular-ly compromised section of flesh, so the best solution to this particular problem was to get rid of it entirely. Thankfully the mouth was a truly amazing part of the body, and healed exceptionally well and very quickly if the area was kept as clean as possible.

"Well, he's done a very good job of it," I pronounced with amusement and Sarah rolled her eyes expressively. "This is one for the books anyway. You don't see very many self-mutilations of the mouth in horses at any rate."

"Can you do anything for him?" one of the stable hands asked anxiously.

"There's very little point in stitching that flap back onto the tongue," I returned, seeing several sad moues appear on the faces of my audience. What did they think I was? Superman? Even if I did suture the flap back together the blood supply to the tissue was hopelessly compromised. It would very rapidly become devitalised, begin to go necrotic and then fall off anyway. And potentially in doing so introduce more serious infection to the rest of the tongue which could prove to be exceptionally problematic. I certainly didn't want to be the one doing surgery on the horse's mouth if I could possibly help it. "Nope, that flap's going to have to come off!"

They looked at me with horror, but I merely smiled back pleasantly.

Using a long syringe with a metal nozzle on the end I flushed out any impacted food material that remained in his mouth, another potential source of infection, before scrubbing the tongue as clean as possible with a chlorhexidine solution. Usually I didn't use this particular surgical scrub very much if I could help it, because too much contact on my skin generally had me coming out in hives, but I thought it was preferential for the animal over an iodine solution.

Applejack didn't much approve of the procedure in any case but considering he had just bitten through his own tongue, I didn't think he ought to have much input into the situation. Just to be on the safe side I administered a small amount of sedation along with pain relief into the vein to ensure he didn't jerk at an inopportune moment.

I clamped off the remaining stubborn bleeder using a pair of long artery forceps I usually kept sterilised in my kit for stopping haemorrhage from uterine arteries during a difficult calving, I applied a ligature to the blood vessel responsible for spilling all that claret onto the floor. A couple of the girls watching over the door turned a whiter shade of pale when they saw me produce the large instruments prompting me to caution everyone;

"If you're feeling in any way queasy, or aren't very good with blood, I suggest you go find something else to do for the next few minutes. I don't want to have to deal with anyone fainting and knocking themselves out on the concrete this afternoon."

My comment made Sarah bark out a laugh and a few of the paler observers disappear from over the stable door. Katie handed me a scalpel blade and within a few seconds I had made a quick, clean incision into the stalk of the flap attaching it to the main body of the tongue. Another smaller vessel began to spurt, receiving the same attention as its compatriot, and then the whole procedure was over and done with.

"Keep it clean with a bit of hibi-scrub over the next couple of days," I informed Sarah as she accompanied us back to the car. I rummaged around for several moments before producing a bottle of thick white antibiotics – which incidentally proved the hard and fast rule that white stuff ought never to go into the vein in horses. "Give him 30ml a day into the muscle for the next three days and he should be as right as rain. I'd probably soften his food for the next couple of days as well so he doesn't have to chew quite so much."

"Will do," she answered, taking the offered medication. There were few horse owners I trusted to be able to inject their animals appropriately, but Sarah was definitely one of them. "If we've anymore problems with the idiot, we'll give you a shout, don't worry about that."

We parted ways and Katie and I returned to the practice, chatting companionably about the case we had just been to see.

"I can't believe he actually managed to bite off his own tongue," the student said part in awe, part repulsed by the whole episode. "I didn't think it was possible!"

"Apparently it is," I returned, more amused than disgusted as everyone else seemed to be. I would never be surprised by the stupid situations that animals – horses in particular – managed to get themselves into. "Applejack certainly had a very good go at it."

"Do you see that sort of thing very often?"

"Not particularly," I said with a shrug. "But animals are quite good at doing strange things to themselves. Yet another funny story to tell my friends the next time we all meet up."

It seemed as though I had a vast collection of them. I didn't know whether it was just me, or the area I happened to work in, but I seemed to have more than my share of entertaining tales from my first year in practice under my belt in comparison.

I returned to the surgery to find that Carl had been sent out on an emergency call to see a fitting dog and was just cleaning my gear when a woman I didn't recognise rushed into reception carrying a cat basket and looking utterly distraught.

"You have to help me!" she gushed at Leah who was on reception, tears streaking her features and her eyes wild with panic.

"My cat is paralysed!"

That got my attention immediately. Some pertinent details were quickly taken before she was ushered into the consulting room and the unfortunate cat, no more than a kitten really, was gently unloaded from the basket onto my table. A pretty tabby and white moggy she remained motionless on the table, her golden eyes wide and tracking my every movement even though she didn't really appear capable of much more.

"Have you any idea what happened?" I queried in a calm professional tone as I conducted a swift neurological exam on the hapless kitten.

My concern was already fairly high, considering the lack of motion from an animal that would usually be squirming all over the place, and it only deepened when I was unable to produce a response to painful stimulus in three out of four feet. And I was squeezing those dainty little pink pads fairly harshly.

Turning off the light I used the ophthalmoscope to assess whether the reflexes of the head were intact, finding to my great relief that the pupils responded appropriately to bright light and her menace responses were intact. It was quite unusual to see this kind of paralysis in an animal this young, unless it had ingested some kind of toxic substance, or had a traumatic injury. I couldn't see any evidence of trauma, and usually if an animal had been poisoned, they came into the practice in an altered state of consciousness, whereas this kitten was fully cognisant of her surroundings.

"I took her to the pet-shop because they are doing free microchipping," the owner said fretfully. "And after they'd done it, she just stopped moving."

My mouth went dry at the implication of what she had just said. I blinked at her momentarily, trying to drop kick my brain once more into gear.

I had a sneaking suspicion as to what was wrong with this little cat. And if I was correct then she needed to be referred to a facility capable of performing spinal surgery straight away. There was one such referral practice about a forty-minute drive from us, but there was only one hitch to the plan. The kitten wasn't insured and the surgery, if it was required, would cost somewhere in the region of three thousand pounds.

"I don't care," the owner said staunchly. Unfortunately, this was something we heard on a relatively regular basis, only to discover that when it came time to hand over payment the owner refused to part with their cash. "I just want her to be fixed! Why? What do you think is wrong?"

I swallowed uncomfortably.

"I think there might have been a problem with the microchipping," I informed her, not wanting to imply that it was the fault of the person who had performed the procedure. I didn't want to get in the middle of a legal suit if it went that way. "I think it might be pressing on her spinal cord, causing this paralysis."

I could have taken some x-rays to confirm my suspicions, but that would all cost money, and would not necessarily be in the best interest of the cat. The longer there was compression on the spinal cord the more likely there were to be permanent damage to that sensitive tissue and increase the potential for there to be swelling within the brain above the source of the compression. I elected not to be the hero and immediately phoned the referral practice. When they heard my concerns, I was instructed to send the cat to them straight away and they would see her as an emergency patient.

Once the client was out the door on the way to the referral practice, I turned to Katie who had stood silent and shocked through the whole consultation.

"And that doesn't happen very often either," I commented half-heartedly. "So today had been a day of unusual occurrences."

Three days later we received word from the referral practice, along with an image of the x-ray they had taken, that my suppositions had been correct. The microchip had lodged between the first and second cervical vertebrae, compressing the spinal cord, causing the clinical signs of paralysis I had been confronted with. I was somewhat astonished by the achievement. I couldn't have hit that particular spot with a microchip needle, which is the same size as many of the needles we used to administer medication to cattle and hard to fit into the relatively tiny intervertebral space in a *cat*, if I had been earnestly trying.

As I was admiring the x-rays, Jess, who had been manning the phones, poked her head around the corner with a wide grin on her face.

"There's a lambing up at Richardson's," she announced. "They've asked for 'the little girl with the small hands'."

My grin matched hers in breadth and I actually leapt about a foot in the air giving a jubilant fist-pump with my good left arm.

"Yes!" I near-shouted triumphantly.

It was an achievement that had never happened to me before with any of our farmers. Usually they asked for Andrew, and sometimes even Carl, but not me. To them I was still the new grad vet who didn't necessarily know what she was doing.

Except now I wasn't. That one simple request for my presence, when they could have so easily asked for either of my employers, meant that I had made it.

"There you go, Kiddo," Jess remarked happily, watching me cavort around the consulting room with a pleased expression on her face. "You're one of the gang now."

Acceptance.

It was a heady thought. At least one of our farm clients believed me to be as equally capable – perhaps even more so at this particular task – than two vets who had been practicing for at least as long as I had been alive.

Despite everything that had gone before in the last eventful year, now I felt as though I was finally a proper vet.

Grabbing my keys, I bolted for the back door, faster than I had ever moved to go out on a lambing before. This was it.

I was accepted.

Now my career was truly beginning.

ABOUT THE AUTHOR

Gwen Inskip is a pseudonym for a veterinary surgeon who graduated in 2011, who then worked in mixed practice for nearly six years before moving into small animal practice due to almost career-ending injuries suffered both on and off the job.

She lives in the scenic North West of England with a collection of spaniels and cats, and her husband who tolerates her disappearing into her writing cave for hours on end to record the almost surreal life experiences that could only happen to a vet.

She enjoys walking, swimming and fiction in all its various guises, and often has to be reminded to put the book down!